As soon as the ░░░░░░░ **lips she realised** ░░░░░░░ **prepared him; sne ought not to have come out with it like that. 'It's true, Blake. I'm having your baby.'**

Her heart stopped beating as she waited for his response, and she did not like what she saw. His eyes narrowed and he looked at her as though she was a complete stranger. As though she was a stranger telling him something he did not want to hear. There was none of the compassion and warmth that had been there a few seconds ago. Nothing but stone-cold disbelief. This was far worse than anything she had ever imagined.

Margaret Mayo was reading Mills & Boon ® romances long before she began to write them. In fact she never had any plans to become a writer. After an idea for a short story popped into her head she was thrilled when it turned into a full-scale novel. Now, over twenty-five years later, she is still happily writing and says she has no intention of stopping.

She lives with her husband Ken in a rural part of Staffordshire, England. Margaret's hobbies are reading, photography, and more recently watercolour painting, which she says has honed her observational skills and is a definite advantage when it comes to writing.

A NIGHT WITH CONSEQUENCES

BY
MARGARET MAYO

MILLS &
BOON

First published in Great Britain 2011
by Mills & Boon, an imprint of Harlequin (UK) Limited,
Eton House, 18-24 Paradise Road, Richmond, Surrey TW9 1SR

© Margaret Mayo 2011

ISBN: 978 0 263 88659 7

Harlequin (UK) policy is to use papers that are natural, renewable and recyclable products and made from wood grown in sustainable forests. The logging and manufacturing process conform to the legal environmental regulations of the country of origin.

Printed and bound in Spain
by Blackprint CPI, Barcelona

A NIGHT WITH CONSEQUENCES

CHAPTER ONE

THIS was an unbelievable opportunity, thought Kara. Flying to Italy with her boss for the firm's annual conference was any woman's dream. She would have liked it to be hers, but unfortunately—sadly—it wasn't. It never could be.

Not that Blake Benedict was a man who could be so easily dismissed. He was aggressively handsome, with strong dark features that guaranteed a second look. And she had stolen many of those. According to gossip he was divorced—acrimoniously—and had sworn never to get married again. But he was not short of girlfriends. Far from it! They vied for his attention like bees around a honeypot.

Not so Kara. She did not want him to notice her, and had always tried to make herself invisible by wearing dark classical suits and little make-up, dragging her hair back unbecomingly. Her hair was actually her crowning glory, a deep, rich auburn, but there was no way she could wear it loose for the office.

The fact that he never gave her a second look told her that her efforts to hide her sexuality really did work. She made a point of being extremely efficient, and even though he rarely heaped praise on her shoulders she knew that he was more than satisfied.

But the very thought of joining him in Italy sent unease curling down her spine. It was impossible. And yet how to tell him? What if he insisted? What if he said that it was part of her job?

She had felt very fortunate when she'd got the position as PA to Blake Benedict, head of the Benedict Corporation—a worldwide organisation whose head office was in London. The agency had lined up another girl, but she had fallen ill at the last minute and Kara had been sent in her place. The first time she had set eyes on him she had felt a whoosh of something dangerous slide through her body. Never, ever in her life had she felt anything like it.

Blake was head and shoulders taller than most men, with a square dimpled jaw and dark, closely cut hair that held a hint of silver at the temples. His grey eyes were deep-set and his nose looked as though it had been chiselled out of fine stone—as did his lips. They were so beautifully moulded that Kara occasionally found herself holding her breath as she envisaged being kissed by them. This feeling was something entirely alien to Kara and unnerved her greatly. She had never kissed a man, never even been out with a man—her father had seen to that! And even though her domineering father was no longer alive his presence still hung over her.

Not that Blake would ever be interested in Kara. She was not beautiful; she was not blonde or gorgeous. She was an ordinary woman with ordinary features and no man ever looked at her twice. But she was the luckiest woman in the world to have landed this job. It had come at just the right time.

'It's not a problem for you, is it?' Blake was surprised that Kara did not look excited. She had not said that she did not want to go, but the look in her eyes reminded him of a doe in a car's headlights and he could not understand why. Their yearly convention was an opportunity every one of his other personal assistants had jumped at.

He had to admit that Kara was different, and if he hadn't been desperate after Olivia had left he would perhaps not have hired her. He liked beautiful women around him and Kara was—well, she made no effort to make herself look glamorous. But she had come with good references and she was damned good at her job. In fact she had made herself indispensable.

And he needed her in Milan. She had dealt with every aspect of the conference; she had practically organised it herself. She knew exactly what the agenda was. So he was going to make very sure that she went with him no matter what excuse she came up with.

She looked extremely nervous, perched on the edge of the chair, and for the first time he noticed what delicate ankles she had—it was all he could see of her legs in the ridiculous long skirts she insisted on wearing. And her flat shoes were the most unflattering things he had ever seen. But her ankles? Why had he never noticed them before? 'Are you going out tonight, Miss Redman?' He had no idea what had prompted the question, but it suddenly seemed important for him to know.

'Is the question relevant, Mr Benedict?'

It was not the answer he'd expected and it amused

him. He even thought that he heard fire in her voice, and there was certainly a spark in her blue eyes. An almost violet-blue. Something else he had never noticed. They were totally amazing when she widened them, when her long silky lashes fluttered as she waited for his reply. This was a new and interesting side to his PA. A side that he felt himself wanting to explore.

Despite that, though, it didn't please him that she was not readily agreeing to his wishes. 'If I am holding you up then perhaps we can have our little talk another time?'

'You're not holding me up.' Kara did her best to ignore the sarcasm he had injected into his voice. 'But there really is nothing to talk about. I can't join you in Italy—it's as simple as that. I'm sorry.'

She held her breath as she waited for his response. She imagined that no one had ever said no to him before. Blake Benedict was law. Everyone jumped at his bidding. And why not, when he was the successful owner of one of the largest IT solutions companies?

Blake's was a success story beyond most people's wildest dreams. It was a story that every member of staff knew. From a little boy of five who'd been able to use a computer better than most adults, he had started his first business venture at the age of sixteen, writing troubleshooting computer programs, and now he had thousands working for him. He was revered by all and no one ever thought of saying no to him. This was why Kara had taken him by surprise. But she simply could not leave her mother even for a few nights. It would be far too dangerous.

Her daring clearly astonished him, though. A deep

frown grooved his brow and narrowed his grey eyes. And when he spoke his voice had developed a hard edge that she was not accustomed to hearing when he spoke to her. 'There is no such word as *can't* in my vocabulary, Miss Redman. I'm sure you've worked for me long enough to know that.'

Of course she had, but her priorities were equally important. 'I—I appreciate what you are saying, but I do have a life outside work and—'

'And that life is so important that you cannot dedicate yourself to your job?'

Kara quivered at the caustic harshness, at the bullet hardness of his eyes, which had turned almost silver, but nevertheless she stuck to her guns. 'Mr Benedict, I do not think you can ever say that I do not do my job properly.' She had worked late so many times that she sometimes felt she spent more time at work than she did at home.

'Maybe not. In fact you're very good,' he admitted.

Grudgingly, she thought. Praise did not come easily from this man. He was a fair employer, though. His staff were treated fairly and paid high wages and they rewarded him by doing their jobs well. Few people left his employ.

Why couldn't he see things from her point of view? Did he not think that his staff had lives of their own?

'So who is it that has priority on your time? A boy-friend, perhaps?' The lift to his brows told her that he clearly thought this was not a good enough excuse.

Kara knew he would not rest until she had told him the truth, or as much of it as she cared to reveal. 'If you must know, I look after my mother. She cannot manage without me.' And she prayed that he would not try to delve any deeper into their circumstances.

For a fraction of a second he hesitated—this was evidently something he had not expected or even thought about. Kara wondered whether he had a mother who equally relied on him. Or maybe not. Blake's work was his life. During the eleven months she had worked for him he had not taken one single day's holiday.

'And there is no one else who can look after her? No other family member?'

Kara was tempted to say, *Would I be talking like this if there was? Don't you think I'd jump at the opportunity of going to Italy?* But she didn't. She lifted her chin instead and met the glare in his eyes with one of her own. 'I'm an only child and my father's dead.' And felt her heart pound as she waited for his response.

His brows lifted fractionally. She would not have noticed if she had not been staring him in the face.

'I see. That is unfortunate. I am sorry.' And he actually looked it. 'What is wrong with your mother?'

'It's her health,' she answered. 'It is not good. She depends on me.'

'And you are sure that there is no one who could possibly keep an eye out for her?'

Kara hesitated. There was her mother's sister, who had always said that she would love to have her stay any time Kara wanted a break, but she had never taken her up on it. It hadn't seemed fair. She wasn't sure that her aunt realised how fragile Lynne had become.

But she'd hesitated too long, and Blake Benedict seized the opportunity, his eyes narrowing on her face. 'I can see from your expression that there is someone.'

Kara compressed her lips and nodded. 'Actually, there is my aunt. Possibly! I would have to ask her.'

'Then do that tonight, Miss Redman. And if the answer is no then I will personally hire a nurse.'

Meaning that he intended her to go to Milan with him whether she wanted to or not! Kara wasn't sure whether to feel annoyed or flattered—it was impossible to decide between the two. She hadn't told Blake the whole truth when she'd said that she could not leave her mother because of her health; it was something far more serious than that. But it was none of his business and she had no intention of talking about it. 'I'll see what my aunt says. Is that all, Mr Benedict?' She kept her eyes level on his in an endeavour to look more confident than she felt. She did not want him to know exactly how fearful she was about leaving her parent.

'That is all.' And already his head was bent over paperwork.

Kara's mother was all for her going. 'Of course I'll stay with Susan. She'll love to have me. She'll let me stay for as long as I like.'

'It will only be for a few days,' Kara hastened to assure her. 'I would get out of it if I could, but Mr Benedict is adamant that he needs me.'

'You worry too much about me, my darling.' Her mother's blue eyes, so much like Kara's, smiled tiredly. 'The change will do me good.'

'Of course I worry,' insisted Kara. 'I have every reason to. You don't think he'll find out where you are?'

Her parent's lips thinned and a deep shadow crossed

her lined face. "You mean the rat who's hounding us for money? Your father certainly didn't do us any favours, did he? But it's unfair that you should have to shoulder the burden. Why all your hard-earned cash should—'

'I don't care about that as long as *you* are all right,' Kara insisted.

'I'll be safe at Susan's,' her mother assured her. 'It's you I'm thinking about. It will do you good to go away.'

Kara tossed her head, her eyes flashing dismissal. 'You're making it sound like a holiday. It won't be, I assure you. Mr Benedict will probably work my fingers to the bone.' The mere thought of going, of being at his beck and call all day, every day, of spending even more time with him than she already did, was not her idea of fun.

'He's realised your true potential, that's what. I bet you're the best PA he's ever had.'

Kara shrugged and smiled, but she didn't tell her mother that Blake Benedict had implied that as well.

'Where are the others?'

Blake had sent a car for Kara and met her at a small private airfield, and as she stepped up into his executive jet she expected the other managers to be already on board. Instead it was empty. The engines were running, they were ready for take-off—and there was only the two of them!

'They've gone on ahead. I thought we could use the time to talk. You have worked for me for almost twelve months and yet you are still a mystery to me.'

His smile told her that he had planned this all along: a

smile designed to put her at her ease, but instead setting alarm bells off in her head. A one-to-one with Blake Benedict was the last thing she wanted. And she could not understand why he was taking this sudden interest. Unless there was something else he was after!

Rumour had it that the last two PAs who had gone with him on these trips had been given their marching orders as soon as they had got back. The rumour machine also said that he'd had affairs with them while they'd been away. Was that what he had in mind? An affair? Did he think it was about time he broke through her personal barrier?

Sheer, cold horror shot down her spine. She had not thought of this before, and it was too late now to back out of the trip. She would need to be careful—erect a shield and not let it slip for even one second.

She felt uneasy at the thought of being at his mercy for the duration of the flight, and when they were cleared for take-off and rose into the air she felt as though she had left her stomach behind. And it wasn't because of the altitude!

It was a luxurious plane, with deep comfortable seats—not that she would have expected anything less—but being on it alone with her employer made everything fade into insignificance. Blake Benedict filled the whole space. It felt as if they were the only two people in the universe.

Which was ridiculous! But how could she help it? She had never found herself in a situation like this before.

Thankfully they had a stewardess, who was prepared to attend to their every need. Except that when Blake insisted Kara sit at his side on a couch so that they could go over the programme of events the woman made herself invisible.

Not surprisingly the laptop lay unattended at his side, and when he half turned in his seat towards her the air in the plane thickened until it became unbearable. Kara had only to inhale to smell the very essence of him. Even if she closed her eyes she could feel him, feel his strength, his omnipotence. Breathing him in was like taking a drug; it settled in every part of her body, making her feel more alive than she ever had in her life.

More aware!

More afraid!

What was happening to her? In all the time she had worked for him she had never felt like this. On the other hand she had never been completely alone with him. Not this alone. It was different in his office—the whole atmosphere was different. She felt awkward now, unsure of herself. Men were a mystery as far as she was concerned.

'You have nothing to fear, Miss Redman. Or may I call you Kara? It's such a pretty name it's a shame not to use it.'

A pretty name! No one had ever said that to her before. A further shiver of awareness ran through her.

'We cannot live together and not be on first name terms.'

'What do you mean, live together?' she asked quickly and sharply, feeling her heart give a giant leap.

'A figure of speech,' he answered, with a lazy shrug and a smile.

A dangerous smile!

'I'm talking about the hotel.'

'Of course,' she answered faintly, hoping that her room was as far away from his as possible. She had booked the whole top two floors but had not been able to stipulate who stayed in which room. They would be allocated on arrival. Except Blake's! He always, but always, stayed in the executive suite.

'I'm glad that you're not wearing one of those terrible suits today.'

Kara felt swift colour rise in her cheeks. She had packed two of her work suits, but she had relaxed her own rules this morning and put on jeans and a spicy pink sweater, completely unaware that the colour complemented her skin colouring and made her look alive and vibrant and very, very pretty—even though she wore no make-up and her hair was tied back in its usual functional style.

Blake too had foregone the dark suits he wore for the office and was wearing an impeccable ivory linen suit which contrasted against the tanned darkness of his skin, making her feel deathly pale by comparison. His jacket had by now been discarded, and although his dark hair was brushed back in its usual style a few strands had been loosened by the wind, making him look younger and less fearsome—and more frighteningly human!

'Why don't you tell me a little more about yourself?' he suggested softly.

A frisson of something Kara failed to recognise shivered through her. It felt dangerous. 'What is there to tell that you don't already know?'

'I know nothing,' he said, 'except that you apparently spend most of your time looking after your mother instead of getting out and enjoying yourself. It's very creditable, of course, but I'm sure she would be the first to agree that you need a life of your own.'

'I am not unhappy doing what I do. Since my father died she has no one—why shouldn't I spend my time with her?' Her voice rose defensively without her even realising it.

'I'm not suggesting that you shouldn't, but you should try and maintain a balance too. You're like me, an only child, so at least we have something in common. What was your childhood like? Did you have lots of friends when you were younger or have you always been a stay-at-home girl?'

'Pretty much,' she admitted.

'Did you have a happy childhood? What was your father like?'

'Why all the questions?' she asked, her voice unconsciously sharp. He had touched a raw spot. There was no way in this world that she was going to tell him what a rotten father she had had, and that even now he was dead he had left them with a whole host of new problems. 'I thought we were supposed to be going over the conference notes?' She inched away from him, curling herself into the corner, unconsciously using the defensive posture she had always adopted when her father threatened her.

Blake's eyes narrowed thoughtfully. 'You're right. It should be business.' But he could not help wondering why Kara was so averse to talking about herself—or her father. Perhaps she had loved him so much that she found the loss still painful? The way she had turned in on herself when he mentioned him suggested that.

He had no idea how long it had been since her father's death, but could not remember her asking for time off to attend his funeral so it must have been before she'd started working for him.

A pity she did not want to talk. He would have enjoyed finding out more about her. She intrigued him. Overnight she had practically turned from an ugly duckling into a swan, knocking him for six in her tight-fitting jeans and hot pink sweater. He had not wanted to take his eyes off her. Unless the dark suits were her office uniform and outside of work she always dressed like this! It would be interesting to see what she had brought with her for the conference.

He opened his laptop, staring at the screen without truly seeing it. All he could see was Kara. The intriguingly, surprisingly beautiful Kara. He could not understand why she kept her raw beauty hidden. She had truly fine features—her nose with a delightful little curve at the tip, amazing blue eyes, and a cupid's bow of infinitely kissable lips. They all begged to be explored.

Kara was glad that Blake had stopped asking questions. She had begun to feel suffocated—or was the rapid beat of her heart caused by a surprising and unwarranted attraction towards him? Her father had banned her from having boyfriends, and even after his death she had never found the time or the inclination. So this was the first occasion she had ever been close to a man who had shown an interest in her, and she found it a scary experience.

When finally Blake began concentrating on the screen in front of him Kara allowed her head to drop back and closed her eyes. But it was not easy ignoring him—not when his cologne teased her nostrils, not when she knew his leg was mere inches away from hers, not when she sensed that sometimes his eyes were on her instead of his computer.

Quite how she managed it Kara did not know, but somehow she fell asleep. She was woken by Blake's light touch on her shoulder as he told her that they were about to land and she needed to put on her seat belt.

Embarrassed now, she moved to her original seat and sat rigidly upright. Blake on the other hand was totally relaxed, a smile turning up the corners of his lips. Had he watched her while she slept? Kara went hot at the thought. Had her mouth fallen open? Had she looked stupid? 'I'm sorry I fell asleep on you,' she said quietly.

'And very beautifully too. It was quite something, having you resting your head on my shoulder. My usually prim and proper PA behaving like a real woman for once.'

Alarm raced through Kara. Her head on his shoulder! Was that what she had done? Her heart went wild, leaping within chest as though it was trying to escape. 'I really am sorry.'

'No need to apologise,' he said, shaking his head. 'It was my pleasure.'

His pleasure! Another source of heat seared the surface of her skin. This was too embarrassing by far. 'It was very rude of me.' She sat up even straighter. 'I didn't sleep very well last night. That must be why.'

'Was it the thought of joining me today that kept you awake?' His grey eyes met and held hers and Kara shivered. There was something in the tone of his voice that alarmed her.

It was wrong to judge all men by her father—but her mother had told her to be careful, that men were not always what they seemed. And all she knew about Blake was that his affairs were legend. There was no way on this earth that she wanted to become another statistic.

But how to answer his question? 'It was the thought of what lay ahead,' she said, which in itself was not an outright lie. 'I've never been to Italy.'

'Then I will enjoy improving your education, showing you places that you have only read about or perhaps seen on the television.'

'Mr Benedict.' Kara put on her most professional demeanour. 'I am sure we will not have time for sight-seeing. You have a very full schedule.'

His slow smile said it all. 'There is always time for enjoyment, Kara.'

CHAPTER TWO

IT SEEMED like no time at all before they were being driven to their hotel, and because Kara had booked the rooms and seen photographs of it she knew what to expect. Except that the grandeur of the building actually took her breath away. The architecture was stunning. But what stopped her breathing altogether was the discovery that her room was right next door to Blake's.

And it was clearly actually part of his suite, because it had an adjoining door. Fortunately locked, but that did not make her any happier, nor ease her alarm. Had he asked for her to be put here?

There was only one way to find out. She walked the few yards along the corridor and tapped on his door, entering at the sound of his voice. 'Why have I been roomed next to you?' she asked bluntly, without even waiting for him to ask what she wanted.

'Does it bother you?' Blake did not look in the least concerned. He did not even look surprised—which told her that he must have been expecting a reaction.

'Actually, yes, it does,' she retorted.

'For what reason?' Grey eyes captured blue.

'Because—well—' She lifted her chin a fraction higher, realising that she actually didn't have a particularly good reason. 'Because it doesn't feel right. I should be with the others. It's as though you're giving me some exalted presence.'

Dark brows rose and he folded his arms across his magnificent chest. He had taken off his jacket and undone the top buttons of his shirt, revealing a scattering of springy dark hairs against darkly tanned skin.

Kara had only ever seen him in a collar and tie. She had never seen the flesh and blood man beneath. Although it shouldn't have affected her, it did. He suddenly looked less daunting and more human. And—she hated to admit it—sexy.

'For your information, I was thinking of practicalities.'

Kara hardly heard what he was saying. She was still staring at his chest, which was quite magnificently muscled. Did he work out somewhere? A private gym, perhaps? Or did he have his own gym? She realised she actually knew nothing about Blake; she had never been interested. But now all sorts of questions sprang into her mind. She was seeing the man now, and not her employer, and could not ignore the way her pulse raced that little bit faster.

'It makes perfect sense,' he said now. 'You are my right-hand woman. You are the trigger to this whole conference running smoothly. There are sure to be things we need to talk about. I need you close to me.'

He needed her close to him! They were the only words that penetrated through the haze that fogged her brain. Close to him!

Then she blinked and everything snapped back into

place. 'I do not agree, Mr Benedict. There is no need for us to—'

Her words were abruptly cut off. 'Miss Redman— Kara—it is too late to change now. The hotel is full.' His expression suggested that she was making a mountain out of a molehill. 'But if it will make you feel any better I promise not to intrude on your privacy.'

Kara felt hot colour flood her cheeks. Was that really what he thought she had been thinking? She somehow managed a glare before turning around and marching back to her room. After her initial concerns she had been excited at the thought of coming here, of hopefully seeing something of Milan, but now new fears began to build. What had happened to the barrier she had supposedly erected? One look at a V of exposed chest and she had gone to pieces. How stupid was that? She was behaving like a teenager instead of a twenty-six-year-old woman.

Unfortunately she would now see Blake Benedict in a completely different light, and it could spoil the whole conference—unless she took herself in hand. Even with his shirt buttoned up and a tie in place, his jacket over his magnificent chest, she would still remember what she had seen. It would still haunt her thoughts and she would hunger to see it again, perhaps to even touch! Oh, God, this was crazy. She was turning into someone she did not recognise.

She needed to be careful. Blake's attitude towards her had changed as well. She knew that. He had never really taken the time to get to know her before. She had been a faceless woman who quietly and efficiently kept his office running. But something had happened on the flight over. He had taken a second look, and a third, and seen a changed person. And if her instincts were anything to go by he was taking a very real interest in her now.

On the other hand maybe she *was* making a mountain out of a molehill. Maybe she was seeing things that were not there. Embarrassment coloured her cheeks again, made her wish that she had not gone to his room. The time to confront him would have been if he had stepped over the mark. It was going to be sheer hell facing him now. It would take all of her courage to keep her chin high and pretend that nothing was wrong.

After unpacking she stepped under the shower. They would soon be attending a pre-conference dinner, where everyone could get to know each other. A supposedly relaxing evening before the work really started. The trouble was that she could not get over her unease that Blake Benedict was on the other side of that door.

Was he showering too? Was he standing there naked? Was all that fabulous flesh exposed? All hell let loose inside her body. Despite the fact that she kept telling herself everything was in her imagination she could not shut him out of her mind.

Which was ridiculous when she thought about it. She had worked with this guy for nearly twelve months and not felt even a second's interest in him—so why was it happening now? Was it because, for the first time, she was seeing him as a human being instead of a man driven by work? Or was it the reverse? Was it because he appeared to be taking an interest in her?

Was that it? Was she falling under his influence? Was it because he was the first man ever to take an interest in her? Please, God, don't let me be so weak as to fall for him, she prayed. Please don't let me be like all the rest.

When it was time to get dressed she was undecided whether to wear one of her work suits or a black dress that she had once bought for a New Year's Eve party she had never actually gone to. It had been only a few months after her father had died and she had felt uncomfortable about leaving her mother. But was the dress too dressy for tonight? Should she save it for the last evening?

As she wasn't used to going out like this she was still debating when a sharp rap came on her door. 'Kara, are you ready?'

Kara groaned inwardly. 'Almost! I'll be down shortly.'

'I'll wait for you.'

Mild panic skittered; goosebumps rose on her skin. 'There's really no need. I can find my own way down.'

'I want you with me.'

It was a command, and Kara knew he would not go away. But she was not going to let him in—not when she was standing in her bra and panties. Embarrassing heat attacked her at the mere thought.

Hastily now, because it was the quickest and easiest, she pulled on the dress. She had already fixed her make-up, but there was no time to do anything with her hair other than a swift flick of the brush.

She opened the door just as his hand was raised to bang on it again. It stayed where it was. He simply stood there looking at her. God, she must look awful. 'Is there something wrong?' She ought to have taken another look in the mirror. 'Am I overdressed? Should I change? I didn't really know what to wear.'

'You look—stunning. Absolutely stunning.'

Blake could not take his eyes off her. The dress fitted her body like a glove—as though she had been poured into it. And what a figure she had! A perfect hourglass! Never before had he seen her dressed like this. Nor had he realised how thick and luxuriant her hair was, or that it was reddish-brown with copper highlights. Wearing it loose made her look sensational. It brushed her shoulders and swung like a silken curtain when she moved.

Why she usually hid herself beneath shapeless clothes he had no idea. Unless it was simply that she thought tailored suits were the correct uniform for work. Which, he suddenly decided, was OK by him.

Otherwise, if she flaunted her fabulous figure as some of the girls in the office did, she would have all the male members of staff drooling over her. And he did not want that. He surprised himself by suddenly feeling very protective towards his PA.

After his welcoming speech to the other delegates he introduced her. 'Gentlemen, may I present to you Kara Redman, my PA? The most competent assistant any man could wish for. She will be at your disposal during the next few days—for work-related reasons only. Anything personal you keep to yourself.'

His last words created the expected laughter but Kara felt embarrassed. She had not dreamed for one moment that he would introduce her so publicly, and for him to say that... Her cheeks burned and she felt on fire.

When the food was served and everyone's attention

was taken she looked at him and said quietly, 'Did you have to make a joke of me?'

Blake's brows rose questioningly. 'It wasn't a joke. It was for your own protection. I've already seen one or two of the men here eyeing you up.'

'And you think I cannot look after myself?' She was totally embarrassed. Admittedly she'd never had to fight men off, but he didn't know that.

'My apologies,' he said drily.

Despite her initial concerns Kara enjoyed the evening far more than she had expected. She enjoyed meeting the people she had been in touch with, putting faces to names, and all seemed to be going well—until after their meal, when everyone mingled and one of the guys from New York suggested to her that she was more to Blake Benedict than his PA.

'What makes you say that?' How could he even think it, yet alone put it into words? Was everyone else thinking the same? Was that why they thought he had made that hands-off statement about her earlier?

'I've seen the way he looks at you. He's like a guard dog on patrol. I just wanted to see if I stood a chance. You are a stunning woman. Any man would give his right arm to go out with you. Blake's a lucky a so-and-so if he's already got you.'

'No one has *got* me,' she retorted, flashing her blue eyes. 'Blake Benedict is my boss and that's all there is to it.'

'Is that so?' he asked with a slow smile, and he moved closer—so close that Kara could feel his breath on her cheek.

She took a step back and felt herself cannon into a rock-hard chest.

'Is everything all right here?'

Blake's voice sounded in her ear and she felt his hand on her waist. The next moment both arms came around her and she was held prisoner against him. Her first instinct was to pull away—but, knowing it would make a fool of him when he was trying to save her from this man's advances, she made herself relax.

Amazingly, her world shifted. She was aware of nothing except the hard strength of his body, the soft thud of his heart against her back—and the pounding of her pulse. These were new and unexpected feelings, and except for the time on the plane she had never been this close to a man. She had certainly never felt her heart flutter because of a man's touch! This was not her employer any more. This was Blake, the man.

For a few mind-blowing seconds they were the only two people in the room. Her heart began its own rollercoaster and her mouth grew dry. She could not speak even if she wanted to, so it was a relief when the other man backed away.

Once he had gone Kara struggled to free herself, feeling mortified now by her reaction to Blake, unable to understand what had come over her. Thank goodness he had no idea that she had been turned on by him. It would be so embarrassing if he knew—if he even suspected it. She put on her most indignant face. 'I am capable of looking after myself.'

'I've no doubt,' he answered calmly, a tiny smile turning up the corners of his mouth, 'but Miles can be very persuasive. He also has a wife at home. I should have warned you that on occasions like this a lot of the guys seem to forget they have other commitments, like wives and families.'

Kara began to realise how little she really knew about men and life. All thanks to her father! But she would learn, and she would learn quickly.

'I've seen the way some of them are already looking at you,' he continued. 'And why should they not? You are incredibly beautiful.'

Kara could not stop a flush of hot blood. No one had ever called her beautiful before. And for it to be her boss! 'It's kind of you to say so,' she said primly, at the same time wishing that she had gone with her first instincts and worn a boring suit. None of this would have happened then. No one would have looked at her twice. 'But, like I said, I don't need a bodyguard.'

'That may be the case,' he admitted, 'but surely you're not going to take away my credit for doing the gallant knight thing?'

Kara laughed. The first time she had really felt comfortable with him. 'For which I thank you. But shouldn't you be mingling with your colleagues, not worrying about me?' She did her best to sound prim again, though was aware that she failed dismally.

'But I do worry, since this is your first conference. I feel obliged to look after you. And I will only *mingle*, as you so delightfully put it, if you accompany me.'

He looked at her with such determination that Kara did not dare refuse. She was conscious, though, as they stopped and talked to each individual in turn, that he was reinforcing the impression that she belonged to him. His hand was on her elbow often as he guided her around the room, and her worst fear was that they would leave together at the end of the evening. And that maybe he would insist on her joining him in his room for a nightcap.

Her heart beat unreasonably fast at the mere thought of it, and the tales she'd heard about his other PAs would not go away. Not that he'd given her any reason for alarm, but even so…

When he was called away for a moment, Kara saw her opportunity and almost ran up the stairs in her haste to escape, closing the door to her room and leaning back against it as though at any moment it would burst open and Blake Benedict would walk in.

It was not until her breathing returned to normal that she realised how stupidly she was behaving. Blake had not said or done anything to make her believe she was in danger, so why was she panicking? Her problem was that she did not know how to handle men. She had never had a boyfriend. She had never even dated. Not one single date. How pathetic was that, at her age?

She got ready for bed and crawled into it but was unable to sleep. Her mind was far too active. Too much was going on in it for her to relax. That Miles man, for instance, and Blake's intervention! She was grateful, but she also felt extremely foolish. He must think her a real *ingénue*.

Finally she heard Blake's door open and close, followed by the murmur of his voice. At first she thought he had someone with him, but then realised he was on the telephone. Even when there was silence she still did not settle down.

Her fertile imagination saw him undressing, and

she couldn't stop herself visualising the hard, strong lines of his body. She even imagined threading her fingers through those dark chest hairs. How would it feel? Would they be soft and springy? Or quite firm? Would the heat of his body transfer itself to her fingers? Would he capture her hand and hold it against his beating heart?

She had absolutely no idea. But she did know that something was happening to her own body just by thinking about it. And if she carried on like this she would get no sleep tonight.

But how to stop her thoughts? These were new feelings. Her body felt vibrantly alive and she could not help wishing that he would unlock the door and tiptoe into her room and slide into bed beside her.

What she would do if he actually did she had no idea. Probably scream at him to go away. Ask him what the hell he thought he was doing. But her body warred with her mind. For the first time ever in her life it burned with excitement.

How she managed to sleep Kara was not sure, but somehow she did. She slept well, and was woken only by her alarm. Feeling self-conscious now about the attention that had been paid to her yesterday, she slipped on a white blouse that fastened right up to the neck and one of her dark suits. Then, as there was still plenty of time before breakfast, she went down to the conference room and put out the notes that would be needed during the day.

She did not hear Blake enter, and gave a tiny cry of alarm when she turned to leave and cannoned right into him.

'Steady, Kara.' And although it wasn't necessary his arms came around her.

Immediately the tantalising smell of his cologne stung her nostrils and the crazy sensations from last night came rushing back, threading their way from her throat right down to her stomach. 'I'm sorry,' she said huskily, at the same time pulling away from him. 'I didn't know you were here.'

'Are you afraid of me?' he asked, a frown pulling his brows together.

'Of course not.' Her reply was instant and fierce, and she looked him straight in the eye. But whether he believed her was another thing. If the truth were known she would not have believed herself.

'Good, because we're going to be spending an awful lot of time together. Have you eaten breakfast yet?' And when she shook her head, 'Then perhaps you will join me and we can go over today's agenda?'

They had already gone over it many times, thought Kara, but refusing did not appear to be an option. The dining room was full, and all eyes were turned on them as they made their way to Blake's table.

Blake had never come across any woman who intrigued him as much as Kara Redman did. He could not make up his mind whether she truly was the innocent she appeared or whether she was putting on an act.

'We're two of a kind, do you know that?'

Kara stopped picking at a croissant and frowned at him. 'What makes you say that?'

'It's simple. We've both lost our fathers, we have no siblings, and we're both career-minded. Maybe my career has taken me on a different path from yours, but you're very good at what you do, very conscientious, which in my eyes makes you the perfect PA. I wish never to lose you.' And that had to be the truth.

'It's very kind of you to say so.'

'Do you mind if I ask how long it's been since your father died? I gained the impression the other day that his death had hit you hard. My father died when I was just eleven, so I've had some time now to get used to it.'

Instantly Kara's face changed. A mask came over it, and when she spoke her voice had become much cooler. Blake instantly felt her withdrawing from him. 'I'd really rather not talk about him, if you don't mind. My father was—well, he wasn't a very nice man. And that's more than I should have told you. I'm sorry.'

'And I'm sorry that I asked.' Her confession had stunned Blake and he wished now that he had said nothing. Kara's hurt still sounded raw. Maybe one day he would discover exactly what sort of man her father had been, but for the time being he needed to bring the conversation round to something pleasant.

'I lived here for a while,' he told her. 'It's a beautiful country. My mother is half Italian.'

To his relief a spark of interest brightened her eyes. 'Does she still live here?'

'Actually, no. She prefers England. Says she likes to be closer to me. But I do have cousins in Seville.'

'And will you be visiting them after the conference? I've never known you take a holiday.'

'I doubt it,' he answered. 'My work means far more to me than spending time looking up relatives. How about you? Where do you go when you take your annual leave?'

Kara shrugged and looked as though she wished he had not asked her *that* question either. 'I stay at home. My mother isn't well enough to travel.'

Of course. He was forgetting her parent's illness. 'In that case you have no right criticising me,' he said, accompanying his words with a smile. Sometimes Kara looked as though she was terrified of him and he had no idea why. She intrigued him, and he felt a very real need to get to know her better while they were here.

Kara found the first day of the conference an eye opener. She was spellbound. Watching Blake take command, the respectful interest everyone had in him, the energy that buzzed around the room, somehow invigorated her as well. She felt more alive than she had in a long time.

She had expected to sit quietly by Blake's side, making notes, feeding him any information he did not have readily to hand, but somehow she found herself being drawn in.

Maybe the fact that she was fully conversant with everything helped. She had made it her business to be the most efficient PA Blake had ever had so that he would never feel the need to get rid of her. And she felt very proud of herself when she was able to answer any question that he threw her way.

'A very successful first day,' he announced when the meeting broke up. 'Thanks to your excellent organisational skills. You've done me proud, Kara, thank you.'

Kara felt swift colour flood her cheeks. 'I only did what I'm getting paid for.'

'And more,' he said, his eyes locking into hers so that she felt a swift river of heat tumble its way through her body. 'Remind me to give you a rise when we get back. For now, I think we should get some air before dinner. We need to stretch our legs.'

Kara was not sure whether this was a command or a suggestion. 'I actually thought of relaxing in my room.' The whole day had proved more exhausting than she had expected.

'Nonsense!' he said briskly. 'You need fresh air and exercise. It's either a walk—I could show you some of the sights Milan has to offer, La Scala for instance— or—' his eyes lit up as he spoke '—we could take advantage of the swimming pool. You do swim, Kara?'

Every nerve in her body shuddered. The mere thought of seeing all that exposed, bronzed, muscle-packed flesh, scared her to death. It was not that she did not want to see him, she did—her heart raced at the thought—but she was afraid that she might give herself away in the process.

'I do,' she answered, unaware that her voice had gone suddenly husky. 'But I think I'd prefer to walk. In any case I haven't packed a swimsuit. I had no idea that swimming was part of the agenda.'

Blake smiled his appreciation at her attempted humour, his eyes crinkling at the corners and making him look—different. Softer, kinder, poles apart from the tough-guy businessman she had got to know so well. This new man frightened her. He sent prickles of heat across her skin and an ache low down in her belly.

'They do have a shop here in the hotel that sells that sort of thing.'

'I'd still rather walk,' answered Kara quietly, since she wasn't being given the option of going back to her room. He was overpowering her, and wasn't giving her any time to herself. And, although she did feel a need to drag some fresh air into her lungs, she could do that just as easily in the hotel gardens—alone!

Amazingly, though, once they set off she began to relax. She even found herself chatting to him as though he was an old friend. Not divulging anything personal, but commenting on the shops that lined the streets, selling jewellery and handbags and all sorts of interesting things. But it was definitely La Scala itself that entranced her.

'I've always wondered about this place,' she exclaimed as they stood looking at the elegant building.

Blake smiled indulgently. 'Do you like opera?'

'Sometimes,' she admitted. 'It depends if I'm in the right mood.'

'And what mood would that be?' he asked, half-turning to face her.

As she met those stunning dark eyes her body flooded with new and different sensations, different emotions that spun her into a whole new world. A world of hunger and desire. A world where there was just Blake and herself. Blake making love to her, teaching her, encouraging her. She felt embarrassed by it. This should not be happening.

But how to help herself? She had the feeling that Blake could read the thoughts in her mind. The countless thoughts that raced round and round, confusing her and worrying her, bringing swift colour to her cheeks, and she wished now that she had gone to her room and shut herself in.

In London Blake was her boss, her employer, and she had never let herself think of him in any other way. She had not even wanted to. But now that she was far away from home, away from the safe and familiar, she was changing, relaxing—and almost welcoming the attention he was paying her.

'When I'm feeling sad,' she admitted in answer to his question, surprised to hear that her voice sounded normal. 'I don't really understand opera, but it somehow helps me. Not that I've ever been to a live performance.'

'Is that so?' Blake's brows lifted. 'Then we will have to see whether we can remedy that while we're here. Watching an opera being performed at La Scala is a serious sensation in itself.'

Swift alarm stabbed at Kara's chest. Attending a concert with Blake went far beyond anything that was reasonable and sane. 'I doubt whether we'll have time.' And even if they had would she really want to go with him? Sit with him for two or three hours, or however long it lasted? This new-found awareness would fill her to such an extent that she would be unable to concentrate on what was going on on the stage. She put on her very best office voice. 'You have a very full schedule, Mr Benedict. And even if you didn't, I doubt you'd get tickets at this late stage. They must be sold out months in advance.'

'Are you trying to get out of it?'

'I am.' There was no point in lying.

Blake laughed at her honesty. 'Tut-tut, Kara. Have

you not realised yet that I always get my own way? And perhaps you could learn to call me Blake?'

There was a whole world of difference between calling him Blake in her mind and saying it to his face. Maybe she was old-fashioned, but using his surname was what she needed more than anything right now. It held up the barrier. It prevented intimacy. It reminded her of who he was.

Not that her body took heed of any barriers. The longer they were together the more aware of him she became. And the more uncomfortable she felt. It was such a foreign feeling that she wanted to turn and run in case he sensed it.

Blake was a man of the world. He knew all about women. If he looked too deeply into her eyes he would be able to see how much he affected her. He would guess at the riot of emotions he had stirred. And he might play on it. Take advantage. Hammer away at her senses until she weakened.

The thought of weakening, of allowing him to flirt and tease, maybe even go further, caused a fast, heart-thumping eruption of excitement, of actual physical need. She turned and began to walk away. Finally she was beginning to appreciate what all the other girls in the office talked about.

'You do understand, Kara—' his voice came closely over her shoulder '—that running away tells me more about you than if you had stayed and argued.'

Blake knew that it was not going to be easy getting Kara Redman to relax in his company. For a few minutes earlier, when they had been window shopping, she had become animated, but as soon as he had suggested doing something that would throw them into close contact she had frozen.

The question was, why? And how long was it going to take him to find out? Kara was the most private person he knew. Other women were always eager to talk about themselves, to show off, to preen like a peacock in front of him. Not so Kara. And the less she opened up the more intrigued he became, the more determined to prise open the shell of security she had wrapped around herself. There had to be a reason and he wanted to know what it was. Whether it really was because of her father or whether it was something else.

'I am not running away.'

He smiled at the hint of defiance in her voice. 'Good, because I want you to relax. I want you to enjoy your time spent here. It's not all about the conference, and since you've never been to Milan before I think you should see something more of the city than the inside of a hotel. In my humble opinion La Scala is the *pièce de résistance*. You cannot possibly leave without embracing a performance here. And I would be honoured to be the one to introduce you to the delights of live opera.'

'It's very kind of you Mr—er—Blake, but your diary is full.'

'As you constantly remind me.' He smiled as he spoke, sensing how difficult it had been for her to use his first name. 'Nevertheless we will make time.' He saw the apprehension in her blue eyes, and the way her teeth bit nervously on her lusciously plump bottom lip— something else he had never noticed before.

He was tempted to kiss away her nervousness, to taste those delicious lips for himself. But he knew that to do so would be fatal. Kara Redman was without a doubt the most intriguing female he had ever come across, and if it was the last thing he did he was going to remove the barriers she had built around herself. And he would take great pleasure in doing so.

'I actually think we should be getting back,' said Kara, looking pointedly at her watch. 'Dinner will be in an hour, and I need to shower and—'

'You are right, of course,' said Blake, but she need not think that he had given up on the opera. The idea of them sitting together watching a performance, her slender body close to his, touching him perhaps, of letting her delicate perfume entrance him, maybe even finding himself far more aware of his surprisingly beautiful assistant than of what was going on onstage, was something that would not go away.

Kara Redman had begun to get beneath his skin like no other woman ever had. He'd been out with lots of beautiful women since his divorce, but their beauty had been skin-deep. His assistant was very different. Once he had really looked at her he had seen a strikingly good-looking woman—and he would never be able to understand why she hid her amazing figure beneath sensible clothes. She was also superbly intelligent. In fact she was one hell of a woman—and he could not believe that he had not realised this months ago.

CHAPTER THREE

RELIEF flooded Kara when she finally got back to her room, and she gulped in great breaths of air. Spending time with Blake left her feeling breathless and exhausted. Crazy feelings swirled in her stomach—desire mixing with unease. Hunger with fear.

What she could not understand was why she was experiencing these feelings now when she never had before. What was the difference between working for him in London and working with him here? The fact was that he'd never taken her walking in London. They had never met outside the office. In fact everything was different.

Even Blake was different. He was no longer the man who barked orders. Who expected them carried out to the letter in the shortest possible time. He had become human. And in so doing he had triggered something inside her that was scary. Because of her father she had always kept her feelings tightly controlled, everything hidden behind a mask.

And when Blake had shown not the least interest in her, when *no* man had shown interest, it had been easy to remain behind her mask of self-preservation. Now it was in danger of slipping. In fact it had already begun its downward slide. A few kind words, a desire to get to know her, and something inside had sprung into life. An amazing new life that both scared and excited her.

As she showered Kara wished with all her heart that she had been able to get out of this conference. Blake could quite easily have managed without her. All the arrangements had been made, the paperwork was done—there was nothing he needed that he hadn't got. She had seen to everything.

She found herself scrubbing at her skin more energetically than was necessary, and asked herself whether she was trying to rid her body as well as her mind of him. Which was laughable! Blake Benedict was not a man anyone could forget easily, and she'd had more than her fill of him over the last eleven months.

It was a wonder she didn't dream about him. Actually, now she remembered she *had*—the very first day of her job. After a gruelling eight hours she had convinced herself that she would never be able to do the job to his satisfaction, and had gone home to bed to experience a dream that had disturbed her deeply. Not because it was erotic—thoughts like that hadn't entered her mind—but because he had assumed the mantle of the devil.

After that she used to tell her mother that she was working for the devil. She had never learned a job so quickly in her life. She had taught herself always to be prepared—and she had been. Always ready with an answer to his quick-fire questions. Until he'd changed from Blake Benedict, business tycoon, to Blake Benedict, human being. A human who was interested in her!

Dressing for dinner, Kara chose the skirt from her black suit, teaming it with a red blouse with a deep

V-neck. Her mother had bought it for her last Christmas, but she had only worn it once, feeling that it was too pretty and too feminine to wear for work.

When she walked into the dining room, taller and more elegant than ever in her black high-heeled sandals, every eye turned in her direction. But the only person she saw was Blake, watching each step that she took.

'You look stunning,' he said softly as he stood to hold out her chair. 'Red suits you. You should wear it more often.'

Kara smiled her thanks, not trusting her voice. He looked particularly handsome too, in a handmade navy suit and a pale blue silk shirt. His red and navy tie, also silk, was as immaculate as always, and as he bent over her, ensuring she was seated comfortably, his cologne— the one he always wore and which was an integral part of him—drifted beneath her nostrils like an aphrodisiac.

And when his hand touched her shoulder, when it lingered longer than was necessary, she felt a shiver of sheer pleasure run all the way down to the tips of her toes. 'You smell divine, Kara,' he whispered in her ear.

So do you, she wanted to say, but could not—dared not. It would be far too intimate. She was not sure that she liked him complimenting her either—not here, not with so many eyes on them.

She was relieved when a waiter placed a napkin on her lap and handed her the menu. Now she could breathe! Except that every breath she drew seemed to bring her nearer to Blake, and when she stole a glance at him from beneath her lashes she saw that instead of studying his own menu he was watching her.

'What's wrong?' she asked, trying to make light of it, which was practically impossible when her heart had just leapt. 'Do I have a spot on my nose?'

'Your nose is delightful. It's a very kissable nose.'

Kara's eyes widened in shock.

'You do not like compliments, Kara?'

The truth was that she was not used to compliments. What made her nose kissable, anyway? It was just a nose. She didn't answer his question.

'As are your lips.'

Kara refused to listen. She did not even look at him any more. She concentrated on the menu instead, ignoring the fact that her stupid pulse had begun to race again and heat was prickling her skin. One of her downfalls was the way that she blushed so easily, and she prayed that her cheeks did not colour now.

Even when their order was placed there was no escape. There was just the two of them. For no reason at all everyone else had faded into the background. Wine was poured and Blake proposed a toast. 'To my most efficient PA—long may you continue to work for me.'

Kara could not drag her eyes away from his. She had never really noticed before how thick his lashes were, or how the grey of his eyes seemed to change colour according to his mood. She had seen them turn a light silver at the office, when someone was being less than efficient, but at this moment, when his attention was concentrated solely on her, when his thoughts were deep and unreadable, they were much, much darker. And they held an expression that she could not read but one that both scared and excited her at the same time.

Here in this beautiful hotel, in this beautiful country,

something was happening to her. It was as though her old life in England was being slowly erased. Memories were fading and something far more exciting was taking over. It was a transitory thing, she knew, but it would surely be foolish not to make the most of it.

He made her feel as though they were the only two people in the room, commanding her attention in such a way that everything except him was blotted out. And for the moment this was all right with her. It was a new experience—one she would treasure when they got back home and everything returned to normal.

She took a sip of her wine and smiled shyly at him. 'You're very kind.'

'It is no more than the truth.'

'I enjoy the job.'

'And are you also enjoying the conference?'

Kara nodded. 'I've never attended anything like this before, and I have to confess I was a little nervous, but, yes, I am enjoying myself.' Except when he paid her too much attention!

'Every man here envies me. And why not, when you are a very beautiful woman?'

This time colour really did flood her cheeks. 'It's very kind of you to say so.'

In response he simply gave her a smile that caused a further skittering of her senses.

The waiter returned with their food and Kara was glad of the respite. It gave her time to take a few deep breaths and tell herself she was in control. That having a man flatter her like this should be a joyful experience, not scary.

And somehow it worked. Gradually she began to

relax and enjoy the evening. She drank more wine than usual, unaware that her eyes were brighter and her cheeks flushed with happiness. They talked incessantly, and Kara laughed out loud at some of his anecdotes.

It was not until the end of the meal, when he passed her an envelope and then watched her face closely as she opened it, that she was suddenly stuck for words. Inside were tickets for *Faust* the following night. Kara blinked twice and swallowed a sudden lump in her throat.

'Think of it as a thank-you from me to you for all the hard work you've put in,' he said, watching the changing expressions on her face.

'I—I don't know what to say. I didn't expect it. I didn't think that you would be able to—'

'But you are pleased?' He looked suddenly anxious, not something he usually did. 'And hopefully a little excited?'

'Yes, but—'

'But nothing, Kara,' he said, his voice firm now. 'All I want is for you to enjoy it.'

Privately Kara doubted whether she would remember anything of the opera. Sitting here talking to him when the room was filled with other people was one thing, but going to the theatre, seated so close that their bodies would touch, when there would be no escape, was another.

She would be far too aware of Blake, of the emotions he was amazingly managing to arouse in her. Alien feelings that sometimes made her feel happy and at others scared her witless.

Admittedly she was beginning to feel more at ease with him. He had never done or said anything to alarm her; he was in fact always the perfect gentleman. So perhaps she was worrying for nothing. It was just that she was not used to being treated so kindly. To have Blake make this generous gesture brought a lump to her throat and tears to her eyes.

Immediately he frowned. 'Now what is wrong? You are still not happy?'

'Of course I'm happy. It's just that no one's ever done anything like this for me before.'

Blake reached across the table and took her hand, enclosing it gently with his other one. 'That is such a pity. You are a gracious woman, Kara, and you should be treated accordingly.'

His sympathy, the look of compassion in his eyes, completely overwhelmed her, and it was a big struggle to control her tears. She swallowed hard and smiled. 'I'm being silly. I'm sorry.'

Blake lifted her hand to his lips. 'I am the one who is sorry. Sorry that you have not enjoyed the pleasures in life that a beautiful woman like you should. But now I think it is time we retired to our rooms.'

Before she made a complete fool of herself in front of everyone—that was what he was saying. Kara smiled weakly and allowed him to take her elbow and lead her upstairs.

CHAPTER FOUR

JOINING Blake for a nightcap went against every one of Kara's self-imposed rules. The trouble was he had a way of making her break them. He had made her laugh tonight; he had been fun company—something she had never imagined her employer being. He had made her almost cry as well, with his generosity.

'What would you like? More wine, perhaps, or coffee? A brandy, even?'

'Coffee, please,' she answered. 'I've already drunk more than I'm used to.' Not that she was drunk or anything like that. She'd only had two glasses, but that was one more than normal. In fact she rarely drank alcohol. Christmas and birthdays were about the sum of it.

Expecting him to lift the phone and order their drinks, Kara was pleasantly surprised when he crossed to the open-plan mini-kitchen at the other end of the immensely spacious sitting area and proceeded to make the coffee himself.

It gave her time to look around the sumptuous suite. Soft cream leather sofas, deep-piled cream rugs gracing American walnut floors, original paintings on the walls, crystal chandeliers. No expense had been spared. The room she was in was furnished well, but this was something else. And she knew what it had cost just to book it for a few days! Almost more than she earned in a year.

Floor-to-ceiling glass doors opened onto a wide balcony, allowing views across the spacious gardens. Well-manicured lawns were softly sculpted by trees and shrubs, and she could see a water fountain in the distance. The swimming pool was not visible, but she knew from the brochure that it was as stunningly attractive as everywhere else.

'Here we are.' Already Blake was joining her, setting out a coffee pot and two china cups on the low table that sat between two of the sofas. Cream and sugar followed.

'I'll pour,' Kara said quickly. It would give her something to do and would stop her from looking at him—at those large capable hands with their perfectly manicured nails. She did not know what had got into her but she could imagine those hands on her skin, holding her, touching her. Arousing her!

Alarm bells rang in her head. Perhaps she ought to leave right now; perhaps it had been a mistake allowing herself to enter his room. When her hand shook as she lifted the pot Blake immediately leaned forward and took it from her. 'Careful, it's very heavy. I should hate you to scald yourself.'

Their coffee safely poured, they both settled back on their seats—opposite each other. Another mistake! He never took his eyes off her. 'I think it's about time that you told me something about yourself, Kara. You've been evasive for far too long.'

A swirl of unease circled her stomach. 'There's not really much to tell that you don't already know.'

'I know you're very wary of men. Who did that to you?'

It was such a direct question that there was no escaping it. But she was silent for so long that he spoke again.

'Was it a boyfriend? Someone who let you down badly? Is that why you—?'

Kara drew in a deep breath, held it for a few seconds, and then let it go quickly. 'My father didn't allow me to have boyfriends. I told you he wasn't very nice, didn't I? The truth is that—that he used to beat me.' There—the words were out, the confession made. The hardest thing she had ever had to do. She looked down at her hands twisting on her lap and did not see Blake's frown, the shock in his eyes. 'I'd really rather not talk about it.'

Her heart began to race and she started shivering, and the next second he was on the sofa beside her, his arms around her, saying nothing but making the sort of shushing noises one would make to a crying baby. It was not until her heart settled, until her body stilled, that he began to murmur words of comfort.

'It's all right, Kara, you're safe with me. No harm will come to you. I will never hurt you, I promise. You can relax. Just close your eyes and relax.'

She heard the words through the thick blanket of her mind. And gradually, as he kept repeating them like a mantra, her father was, for once, amazingly forgotten. She was aware only of Blake's warmth, of the strong arms holding her, of his heartbeat against her body.

And when he touched his fingers to her chin and

turned her face up to his she saw not her employer, not Blake Benedict tough businessman, but warm, human Blake. A Blake whose grey eyes were soft with concern. Without even realising what she was doing she snuggled up closer.

Never in her life had she felt as safe as she did now. No man had ever held her like this, made her feel secure, as though her whole world had turned around and no one would ever mistreat her again. She had not believed it possible. And for it to be her employer, of all people! Her father had always drummed it into her that she was a worthless creature whom no man would ever look at twice. He had said it so often that she had believed it.

Kara knew that she ought to move now that she had recovered, but pulling away from Blake was the last thing she wanted. And Blake seemed in no hurry to let her go either.

'Are you sure you don't want to talk about it?' he enquired softly. 'It might help.'

'No, I'm sorry. I couldn't.' It was too humiliating by far. Even though her father was dead she still did not want to talk about him. 'I never will. And I'm sorry I—'

'Do not keep apologising, Kara. I'm glad that you've told me. It helps me to understand you.' He trailed a gentle finger down the side of her face, pausing a moment before tracing the outline of her lips. Then he touched her fingers to his mouth and kissed them before placing them against her lips again. 'You're a beautiful lady, both inside and out, and you do not deserve to have gone through what you have. I reiterate my promise that I will never do anything to hurt you.'

Kara let out her breath slowly, feeling her body relax. She liked him holding her, she liked him touching her, she liked what he was saying to her. It was almost as though she had been transported into a different world— a world where everything was beautiful and sensual and no one ever hurt anyone. A world she had never known before.

'Maybe you should drink your coffee,' he said, 'before it gets cold.'

'I'd rather you held me a little longer.' The words slipped out before she could stop them and she was horrified. 'I'm sorry. I'm being silly. I shouldn't have said that.'

'My beautiful Kara, I'm glad that you did. It proves that you trust me.' His eyes had darkened but they still held the softness, the tenderness, and Kara guessed that he had never held a woman like this before and not kissed her.

She was grateful to him. And she actually experienced a sense of relief that she had told him about her father. It felt cathartic—as though a whole weight had been lifted from her shoulders, finally giving her permission to move on.

He continued to stroke the side of her face, gently sweeping back tendrils of hair that got in his way, and Kara enjoyed the touch of his fingers so much that when he again traced the outline of her lips they parted of their own volition, the tip of her tongue coming out to touch and taste him.

She heard the faint groan in the back of his throat and had no idea what it meant. Was he saying *please don't do that*? Or, *if you do I won't be responsible for my actions*? It was embarrassing to be totally innocent in the ways of men.

And the trouble was that the longer she remained in his arms the more intense her emotions became. She reached out and touched his cheek, feeling the faint rasp where his strong black hair was already growing again. He put his hand over hers, holding it there for a few seconds before moving it slowly so that he could press his lips to her palm.

Then he folded her fingers over the kiss and gave her her hand back. 'Especially for you, my troubled one.'

Kara did not want her hand back; she wanted to continue to touch him. She wanted to trace the outline of his face, his beautifully sculpted lips. She wanted— When she suddenly realised exactly what it was that she wanted it took her breath away. She wanted him to kiss her—really kiss her. Something she had shied away from all her life. She had shied away from any sort of contact with a man.

But Blake was more than just a man! She closed her eyes and thought about what it would be like for him to kiss her. Would it be light and sweet, or deep and tempestuous? Would it fill her with pleasure or dread? She felt him move and guessed that he was going to put her away from him, move back to the other sofa—with the coffee pot between them. And her heart suddenly ached.

But then she discovered that he was simply positioning himself more comfortably in order *to* kiss her. It was a gentle kiss, an experimental kiss, but the touch of his lips on hers was like lighting the touchpaper on a firework. It fizzed quietly at first, but then exploded into a galaxy of sparks and showers, of crackling noises and body-tingling sensations.

Sensations such as she had never experienced before. Stimulation such as she had never experienced before. *Whoa!* she thought. What was happening here? How could a simple kiss create such strong feelings? Except that it was not simple. It was a complex kiss, one that spun into every corner of her body, creating tingles and hunger and all sorts of crazy emotions. It was like pins and needles everywhere.

She was afraid to open her eyes and look at him. This was a man of the world who had made love to endless women. Experienced women. Women who would readily respond. Whereas all she was doing was submitting. It would hardly be enough for him.

But letting him know what he was doing to her, what was happening to her, felt frighteningly like revealing her soul. Shame suddenly crept over her, shame that she was allowing the kiss, and she struggled to free herself.

Immediately Blake let her go. 'I'm sorry, Kara, I thought you were ready for this. I want to help you—if I may be permitted to do so? Not all men are the same. You need to know that. There are some good guys around.'

Finally she looked at him. And what she saw in his face was nothing but compassion. He was not judging her or comparing her. 'I'm sorry,' she said, her voice no more than a husky whisper now. 'It's just that I'm not used to—'

'I know and I understand. I'm sorry I misjudged the

timing,' he said gruffly. 'Go to your room if you want to.' And he did indeed look truly sorry. Sad, even.

Kara did not want to leave; she did not want to be alone—not yet. She wanted to feel Blake's strong arms around her again. They had held comfort and—and something else she could not put a name to. 'Will you—will you just hold me?' she asked, feeling tears gathering in her eyes.

His answer was to pull her gently against him, his arms folding round her. How long they sat there like that Kara did not know, but it felt like a very long time. She could feel the regular beat of his heart and peace stole over her until gradually she felt completely at ease with him.

The threatened tears never materialized, and when she eventually went back to her room she felt like a new woman. She even—and this thought really scared her—wondered what it would feel like to have Blake in bed beside her. Except that she knew it would be hard for him, if not impossible, to sleep with her and not want to make love. But she was not ready for that yet.

Her mind was slowly adjusting to the idea that such a relationship could work without her feeling that she was doing something wrong, something her father would not approve of. But he had been such a big influence in her life that it was too soon yet to let go of the old and welcome the new.

At least she was getting there.

Blake's eyes caught Kara's as she joined the conference the next day. Her confession last night had knocked him for six. Any man who hurt a woman, whether it was physically or verbally, was the lowest of the low as far as he was concerned. And her father's abuse had certainly left Kara with some problems.

She had trembled so much when he had held her that he had feared she might break down. It was a miracle that she had grown into the competent woman she was. Clearly work had been her saviour. Only when she was working was she in control of herself.

Certainly she had been on edge in his suite. He had felt her fear. But then, surprisingly, she had let him kiss her. It had taken every ounce of his not inconsiderable self-control to contain the kiss. How he had managed it he was not sure, and as delicate as it had been it had still sent a raging heat through his body.

Kara had no idea how lovely she was—how sexy, how alluring. He could understand now why she always dressed down, why she never made anything of herself. If she dressed as most of the other women in the office did then she would have every man in the company after her. And that, he realised now, was the last thing he wanted.

She did not know it, but after he had kissed her her eyes had assumed a sparkle he had never seen before, and her skin had glowed. It had been the hardest thing in the world not to kiss her again. And even harder to let her return to her room!

'Are you all right?' he asked her now. 'Did you sleep well?'

'Yes, thank you,' she answered, her eyes meeting his shyly. 'And I'm sorry about last night.'

He shook his head. 'Think nothing of it. You have nothing to be sorry for.' He was the one who was sorry—sorry that she had been caused such suffering at the hands of a monster like her father. His blood still boiled every time he thought about it.

'It actually helped, telling someone,' she admitted with a wry twist to her lips. 'I didn't think it would. I've kept it bottled up all these years. But when I went back to my room I felt a sense of relief. I slept better than I've done in a long time.'

'Then I'm glad that I could be of service.' How any man could treat his daughter like that he had no idea. It was perhaps fortunate that he was no longer alive or he would have felt like confronting him, giving him a taste of his own medicine. He wasn't usually a violent man, but anyone who could harm his own flesh and blood did not deserve to be treated humanely.

'And the opera tonight? Are you looking forward to that too?'

Kara nodded. 'Actually, yes, I am.' After last night she felt much more at ease with Blake. Whether it was because he now knew something about her past, or because she had spent so much time with him and got to know him better she wasn't sure. But she was beginning to see him as a man instead of her boss. A good-looking, sexy man who had lit a fire inside her. The idea that confession was good for the soul had certainly been true in her case. She felt as though a great big weight had been lifted from her shoulders and now there was a whole bright new future ahead.

'I thought we might have dinner somewhere first. Unless you'd prefer to eat after the theatre?'

'I think before.' She could imagine that a late dinner would lead to a late evening, and that could lead to…

Kara allowed her thoughts to go no further. The way she had relaxed in Blake's company last night, responded to him, still scared her slightly. It was hard to get it out of her mind.

'What do I wear?' she asked him now. 'I'm not sure I have anything suitable.'

Blake smiled. 'The black dress you wore the other night will be perfect, Kara.'

Dinner was everything Kara had expected it to be. The restaurant was not far from the theatre, and served exquisite food in stunning surroundings. She chose sole fillet with asparagus for her main course, and it was truly the most delicious fish she had ever eaten.

But her attention was not on the food. It was on Blake instead. Ever since that kiss he had filled her body and her mind, and she was beginning to wonder whether it was wise spending so much time with him. Her heart seemed to have developed a mind of its own, fluttering like a captured bird whenever he spoke to her, whenever he was near.

'What are you thinking?'

His voice was low and gruff and it created an unimaginable stream of sensations that sped through her body like a fast-flowing waterfall. Sitting opposite him like this, feeling his oh-so-attractive grey eyes constantly on her, was not a situation she felt comfortable with. 'I was actually wondering what I'm doing here.'

An instant frown caused his dark brows to scurry together. 'You are not looking forward to the opera?'

'Of course I am. But—' How could she explain how

she felt? 'I'm actually nervous about spending time with you.'

Blake reached across the table and rested his hand on her arm. 'Kara, all I want is for you to enjoy some free time, which I fear has been lacking in your life.'

He dared not say that besides wanting to spend time getting to know her he wanted to make love with her. It would send her scuttling for shelter more quickly than if she was fleeing a thunderstorm. But the truth was the more time he spent with her, the more excited his body became, the more hungry he grew. Kara was without a doubt one very intriguing female—sexier, he guessed, than she had ever dreamt she could be. She lit fires within him that would never be assuaged until he had made her his. But he would never, ever force himself on her. If and when they did make love it would be because she wanted it too.

'I do trust you, Blake,' she said now, her eyes wide and beautiful and more violet than blue.

He wished that she had not used those words because it made him feel ashamed of his thoughts. He squeezed her hand and then let it go.

Faust was everything Kara had expected—and more. She sat entranced throughout the whole performance, hardly even aware of Blake at her side, or the fact that his eyes were often on her, or that his hand held hers. Tears ran down her cheeks at the end, when Marguerite mounted the scaffold where she was to be hanged for killing her child—Faust's child.

Blake produced a handkerchief and dabbed at her

tears. At the same time his arm came around her, holding her firmly against him.

'That was lovely,' she managed to say. 'I truly enjoyed it.'

'And that is why you are crying?'

'It was sad, but beautiful too. Thank you for tonight. It is an evening I will always remember.'

In the car on their way back to the hotel Kara did not mind when he put his arm around her again. She nestled her head on his shoulder and closed her eyes. She felt as though she was in another world—a world where bad things never happened, where there was light and laughter...and Blake!

If anyone had asked her a few weeks ago whether she fancied her boss she would have laughed at them, would have declared herself a man-free zone. But all that was changing, and Blake was the reason. He was giving her confidence in herself, assuring her that she was a very beautiful woman—and at the same time revealing that he was enchanted by her. Blake Benedict enchanted by her! It was the stuff of dreams.

'Shall we indulge in a nightcap?' he asked as they stepped out of the private lift that had swiftly taken them up to his suite.

Kara surprised herself by agreeing. She had enjoyed his company so much this evening that she did not want to be on her own again yet. There was something about Blake here in Italy that was different. He was charming and considerate and she truly felt relaxed with a man for the very first time in her life.

'What would you like?' he asked. 'Brandy, perhaps? Or maybe wine?'

'Actually, coffee would be good—if that doesn't sound too boring?'

'Coffee it is, then, and it doesn't sound in the least boring. In fact it's probably wise.'

He lifted the phone as he spoke, and Kara loved hearing him speak in Italian. It made him seem excitingly different. It added to the glamour of the evening. It was hard to believe that she was here again with her boss at this time of night and they were going to settle down for a quiet drink together. She needed to be fresh and alert tomorrow. Perhaps it had been a mistake coming here. Maybe she ought to have gone straight to her room and to bed.

And in the end it was the coffee that proved to be her undoing. As she sat opposite Blake in a deep comfortable chair, nervously aware that his eyes never left her, Kara's hand trembled as she took a sip of her drink and some of the hot liquid spilled down the front of her dress.

Instantly Blake jumped up, took the cup from her, and began dabbing his handkerchief on the stain. It was a much too intimate gesture, and Kara's heart began to thud painfully against her ribcage—especially when he draped his arm around her shoulders to hold her steady. 'It's all right, Blake, it's nothing. I—'

Her words were cut off when his eyes met hers, when she saw the dark hunger in them, when all the breath seemed to leave her body.

'Forgive me—I have to do this,' he said, his voice rougher than she had ever heard it. And she swiftly realised that he wasn't talking about the damp mark on her dress, but something far more intimate.

And, amazingly, this time her lips were ready for his. The rhythm of her heart altered and she closed her eyes. Why fight the inevitable? All evening she had been far too aware of Blake to not want to experience his kiss again.

Blake quickly realised that what he had intended as a gentle kiss, not wanting to frighten her, or rush her into anything that she was still not ready for, was swiftly turning into something else. Kara's lips had parted on a sigh that suggested secret desire, and when he cautiously deepened the kiss, when he felt her response, when she kissed him back with a hunger that took him by surprise, he was unable to stop himself.

Fire built between them as their tongues entwined and danced and tasted and explored, as he nibbled her lower lip and she did the same to him. Every pulse in his body threatened to explode. And he knew that it would take every ounce of self-control to put her away from him afterwards.

Kara found it difficult to breathe; she could not understand what was happening to her. How could she allow Blake to kiss her like this? How could she want his kiss when she had always hated men with a vengeance? The lure had been building from day one, and the taster she'd had yesterday had woken something inside her, but even so...

Cautiously she risked looking at him, and her breath caught in her throat when she saw the raw desire in his eyes—gone in an instant, shielded from her gaze. If any man had looked at her like that in the past she would have run a mile, but she knew without a shadow of doubt that Blake would never pressure her into anything that she was not ready for.

And the fact was—and this was as much of a surprise to her as it would be to Blake—she actually wanted him to make love to her.

She closed her eyes again, allowing the moment to seep into her mind, into her bones, into her heart, feeling an unaccustomed ache in the lower regions of her stomach. If Blake ended the kiss now she would feel bereft. She would have had a taste of heaven snatched away from her as quickly as it had arisen.

Of their own volition her arms snaked around him, trapping him, her body urging itself against his raw masculine hardness. It shocked and excited her at the same time. Never in her wildest dreams had she ever envisaged that she would be in a situation like this.

The wild throb of his heart beating against her own told her without words that excitement ran through his veins too, and that he was also deeply affected by what was happening.

Why, she asked herself, when for nearly a year she had worked for this man without ever feeling anything, was this happening now? No, that was wrong. She *had* been aware of him; how could any woman not be? But her fears were such that she had allowed her thoughts no purchase.

Now they were in danger of escaping the tight confines she had kept on them—in fact they had already escaped. They were not at the galloping stage yet, but they were sufficiently free of their reins to taste freedom. And, oh, how she liked it.

Based on pure instinct now, she ground her hips

against him, shocked by his hardness, but actually glorying in the fact that she was able to do this to a man. To Blake. Not *any* man—never any man. Would he allow her to set the pace? Already she was in danger of running rather than walking, and she could hear the drumbeats of her heart echoing in her ears.

Words seemed irrelevant. Words would shatter the atmosphere that cocooned them. And when Blake trailed his fingers down the exposed arch of her throat, pausing on the fluttering pulse he found there before moving lower to feel the soft swell of her breast, Kara's breath caught in her throat. Her eyes fluttered open.

Blake was watching her, gauging her reaction, but she saw behind the reassurance he sought a hunger that matched her own. The grey of his eyes had deepened to charcoal, almost blending with the blackness of his pupils, though when he saw her looking at him he instantly lowered his lashes.

Kiss followed kiss followed kiss—deep, heartstopping kisses that sent her spinning into a world she did not recognise, a world where senses were paramount. In these last few minutes she had become a woman—a woman filled with emotions she had often wondered about but never expected to experience. She felt as though she had been born again. And she wanted this moment to go on for ever.

It was disappointing, therefore, when Blake lifted his head, when his hands fell to his sides. Her first thought was that she had let him down, and she felt tears welling—until he tentatively suggested that they make themselves more comfortable.

Which must be why they ended up in bed!

Kara could only vaguely remember Blake lifting her into his arms and carrying her to his bedroom. For some reason her mind had gone numb. She had been aware of nothing except the feelings churning round and round inside her—feelings that needed both feeding and assuaging.

What had begun as a tingle had developed into a stampede of pulses, of hot pounding blood, of her heart beating so hard and so fast that she was afraid it would burst.

And all because he had kissed her!

Except that a kiss from Blake was more than just a kiss. It was a full-scale attack on her defences. It stripped away barriers, leaving her open and vulnerable. And bursting with excitement! If this was what making love was all about then she was glad that she had not gone through her whole life without ever knowing what she was missing.

Their kisses became more intense, more hungry, more *everything*, in fact. Not only did he kiss her mouth, make it his, sucking and nibbling, creating deep wells of passion that both shocked and thrilled her, he trailed kisses down the arch of her throat, causing her head to fall back in utter abandonment, and somehow he managed to remove her clothes at the same time.

When she heard his swift intake of breath Kara did not know what was the matter—until she felt his fingers touch a certain place on her back. Then she knew!

'How did you get this scar?' he asked, his voice unusually quiet.

Kara struggled with the truth, but decided that she needed to be honest. 'It's from the buckle on my father's belt. He didn't mean to hurt me that badly.' Not that he had ever said that, or even apologised. He'd been blind drunk at the time.

'Whether he meant it or not, it should never have happened,' growled Blake. 'Did he beat your mother as well?'

Kara nodded.

Blake swore.

'It's a good job he is no longer alive or I would have great difficulty in keeping my hands off him. Only cowards hit women. Did you never report him, Kara?'

'I was too afraid,' she confessed. 'He was a very big man. He'd probably have killed me.'

Blake swore again under his breath and cradled Kara in his arms. He held her for a long time, until he felt them both relax again, until he was able to push to the back of his mind everything that was bad and evil.

'You are so brave,' he told her, over and over again. 'Brave and beautiful.' He kept stroking her skin, and when she lifted her lips up to his he groaned and kissed her, and his heart leapt when she took his hand and put it on her breast.

Kara closed her eyes and gave herself up to the moment. Blake's touch caused her breasts to engorge and become incredibly sensitive, and the moment when her nipples tightened into excruciatingly responsive buds was an experience she would remember for the rest of her life, even if it never happened again.

But even that feeling increased when he kissed her breasts, sucking her tingling nipples into his mouth, nipping them with his fine white teeth, until every one of her bones melted.

'You are all right with this?'

Blake's voice was gruff and hoarse, and his eyes, raised to hers, held an expression that shook her rigid. They were filled with an emotion that suggested he was in the grip of something much stronger than himself, something he was struggling to control.

And it was all because of her!

How could that be? How could kissing her do this to him? She was inexperienced, she didn't know what was expected of her, and she wasn't even very pretty. She was—

'Kara?'

She looked at him, unaware that her eyes were huge and shiny, that her cheeks were flushed and she already looked as though she had been well and truly made love to.

'Do you want me to stop?'

She rocked her head from side to side, not trusting herself to speak. How could she when both her body and mind felt as though they no longer belonged to her? Somehow he had cast his spell over her and she was now his to do with as he liked. She had gone from being a woman who was afraid of men to someone whose body was filled with a desperate need to be touched.

Needing no further encouragement, Blake trailed kisses across the divide from her breasts to her navel. All she had to do was lie there and enjoy! *All she had to do!* It was impossible. She could not keep a limb still. She wriggled and squirmed and was completely unaware of the sounds she made—sighs and cries, even tiny screams of pain. Yet it wasn't pain at all.

And Blake was enjoying making her aware of her

body, of its erogenous zones, of the sensations just the lightest touch of his fingers or tongue could create. It was almost an act of cruelty. Delicious, mind-blowing cruelty.

But none of it—nothing—prepared her for the moment when he explored the most intimate part of her. She was shocked and stunned when she discovered how swollen and sensitive she had become, how moist, how responsive she was to his touch, how her body seemed to arch so that he could explore her more fully. She had never in her life known that such sensations existed, that simply by touch she could feel ready to explode.

Her fingernails dug into his shoulders, her body lifting from the bed almost of its own volition. 'Make love to me, Blake,' she said hoarsely, almost without knowing that she spoke. 'I want you to make love to me.'

'If you're sure?' His voice was as hoarse as her own.

'I'm sure.'

And when he finally lowered himself over her, when he began to enter her, protecting himself first, she could hardly breathe. She was shocked, therefore, when he stopped, when she heard him swear softly.

Was she doing something wrong? She wasn't experienced like his other girlfriends—was that it? Should she be doing something? Helping him? Sadly, she had no idea.

'Blake?'

'You're a virgin.' The words choked from his throat. 'I thought you knew that.'

'What I mean is that I cannot do this to you. I've never made love to a virgin before. It would be wrong to—'

Kara touched a finger to his lips. 'You're not doing anything I do not want. Please, Blake—please don't leave me like this. I want it as much as you do.' And she wrapped her legs even more tightly around his hips, grinding herself against him.

Blake groaned again, and after only a moment's further hesitation plunged himself into her.

She felt a brief moment of pain, and then came the pleasure. Intense, mind-blowing pleasure.

'Blake!' Kara heard herself call his name over and over again, felt her hands clawing his back, heard him telling her that it was all right to let go.

And seconds later her world exploded.

CHAPTER FIVE

IT WAS the last day of the conference. As Kara walked into the room she felt sure that every person present must know that she had let Blake make love to her last night. Her reflection as she brushed her hair had shown a different woman. A woman with stars in her eyes and a bloom to her skin. A woman who had well and truly been made love to.

She had spent the whole night in Blake's bed, only returning to her room this morning to shower and dress. She had not gone down to breakfast—food was the last thing on her mind. And now she was afraid to look at Blake, because she knew that if she did her hormones would jump all over the place again.

'You were amazing last night,' he whispered when she reached his side. 'I trust you have no regrets?'

'We shouldn't be talking like this,' she whispered fiercely. 'Let's get on with things.' Even so, she was unable to really concentrate, too conscious of what had gone on between them, and she was relieved when at lunchtime the conference finally drew to an end.

Blake's closing speech included his thanks to her for all the hard work she had put in both prior to and during the last three days. 'I do not know what I would have done without my wonderful PA,' he said. 'The fact that everything has gone without a hitch is all down to Kara. Her organisational skills are second to none. I think a round of applause is in order.'

Hot colour flushed her cheeks as every pair of eyes turned on her. 'I only did my job,' she muttered, smiling awkwardly. And when he presented her with a bouquet of pink roses she was even more self-conscious.

'You deserve some recognition,' he said firmly. 'None of my other assistants has ever reached your high standards. I can fault you on nothing.'

It was not until they had said their goodbyes to everyone and finally gone up to his suite that he shocked her still further. 'I have another surprise for you.'

His voice was no more than a low growl in his throat now, and it sent a shiver of expectation across Kara's skin. She braved a glance at him and saw the way that his lips were trying to contain a grin. He looked, she thought, like a little boy who was doing his best not to give away a secret.

'A reward for a job well done.'

She waited.

'We're going on a few days' holiday.'

Kara's mouth fell open. She could not help it. This was the last thing she had expected. 'What do you mean, a holiday? I can't. I have my mother to think of. I couldn't possibly leave her any longer.' Even though the thought of spending more time with Blake was exciting, her mother was her top priority. Besides, Blake *never* took holidays. What was he talking about?

'She doesn't like staying with her sister?' he asked, a

sudden frown replacing his smile. 'Or—are you perhaps afraid of what is happening between us?'

Kara was glad that they had left the others behind. This was not a conversation she wanted anyone else to hear. 'I'm not afraid.' The denial was instant, but she could see that he did not believe her. 'My mother relies on me. She needs me. And it will be too much for Aunt Susan if she has to look after her for any longer.'

Dark brows lifted. 'I think maybe we should let your aunt be the judge of that. Why don't you call her?'

It sounded as though he was giving her no choice. And, although she would have dearly loved to spend more time with him, making magical love—and it had truly been magical—she knew that it would be impossible. 'You do not fully realise my situation. I'm sorry, Blake, but—'

'I'm not forcing you to stay,' Blake said, trying to make his voice sound as gentle and persuasive as possible. 'But I do think you deserve some relaxation. You've worked very hard and I'd like to show you my appreciation.' She enchanted him, and one night of passion was not enough. He wanted to spend more time with her. Taking her virginity and then coldly dismissing her to resume normal office life was not what he wanted. She deserved better. He wanted her to know that it had not been a one-off. He did not want her to think ill of him.

Not that he was looking for anything long-term. He had no intention of settling with any woman ever again. To hell with all that. One go at marriage was enough. But at least he could show Kara that not all men were bad.

'OK, I'll ring my mother,' she said, still sounding reluctant, 'and see what she says. Maybe a couple of days. I don't want to lumber Aunt Susan with her for too much longer.'

Blake would have liked to spend more than two days with her, but he knew that to push the issue would end up with her refusing to go with him at all. 'I'm sure you won't regret it,' he said, touching his hands lightly to her shoulders and dropping a kiss on her cheek.

The sweet, dewy softness of her skin and the intoxicating smell of her was almost his undoing. What he really wanted to do was kiss her and pleasure her again. But he did not want her to think that he was using sex as a way of persuasion, so he reluctantly backed away, leaving Kara to go to her room.

Her mother, surprisingly, was happy for her to stay longer. 'You deserve a break,' she said. 'And your aunt is glad of my company'

'Everything is all right?'

'Of course. I'm safe here, Kara.'

Kara knew what she meant. Her biggest fear was that the loan shark her father had lumbered them with might catch up with her.

Her father, as well as being a bully and a tyrant, had taken out a loan in her mother's name, telling her that it made good business sense for tax purposes. Her mother had been too frightened of him to argue. His building company had begun to go downhill because he had spent most of his money on gambling and drinking, but it had not been until after his death that they'd discovered the loan had never been repaid and that exorbitant interest rates made it look as though it never would be.

The man after their money was a sharp-faced, cold-hearted individual, without an ounce of compassion. She could not leave her mother to deal with him. Even thinking about him caused her to shudder. But she could not tell Blake about him either. Her mother did not want anyone to know. She found the shame of the whole situation too embarrassing, even though it was most of Kara's salary that went towards paying off the debt.

Kara quickly packed and drew in several deep, steadying breaths before taking the few steps along the corridor back to Blake's room. His door was open, as though he was waiting for her. And his suitcase was also ready to go. His brows rose as he waited for her to speak.

'I'll come with you,' she said quietly.

'Your mother and aunt are all right with it?'

'Yes.'

'But you are not?'

'I've never been on holiday with a man.' In fact she had never been on holiday. Even saying those words caused her heart to flutter alarmingly. Would she be throwing herself in at the deep end without being able to swim? Would she regret it? Would she lose her job because of it? A multitude of questions swam through her mind.

'You are afraid of me?'

Not Blake. It was her feelings that she was afraid of. She was afraid that at the other end of the spectrum it would all be too much for her, that she would never want it to end. That she would have a taste of heaven before going back to her own private hell.

Although she did not disclose her thoughts, the conflict in her eyes was clear for Blake to see. With a groan he pulled her against him. 'You have nothing to fear, Kara, not while you're with me. I want you to be happy, that is all. You've looked tired this last couple of days. I guess I've put too much pressure on you. Let this be my way of saying thank you.'

Kara buried her head in his shoulder, feeling stupid tears again. God, why did this man always make her want to cry? The plain fact was that no one had ever been this kind to her before, and she was totally overwhelmed.

'Are you packed?' he asked, gently putting her away from him.

Kara nodded.

'Then let's go.'

'Where are you taking me?'

He smiled—the sort of smile that flipped her heart and made her want to lift up her face for his kiss.

'I'll let that be a surprise.'

A car and driver were waiting, and on the journey Kara spent her time looking at the stunning landscape, trying to ignore the fact that she was with her boss and that she had spent last night in his bed. Even sitting beside him, not even touching, she was overwhelmed by the feelings he managed to arouse.

Finally they arrived at a beautiful white villa overlooking the shores of a huge lake.

'Welcome to Lake Como,' he said. 'And to what used to be my grandmother's house.'

Kara's eyes were as big as saucers. 'Who lives here now?'

'No one permanently,' he admitted. 'Since her death it's been kept for any family member to use. I suppose you'd call it a holiday villa.'

A holiday villa! That had to be the understatement of the year. Who could afford to keep a villa like this and not use it? She truly was moving in exalted circles.

'Is anyone else staying here at the moment?'

Blake shook his head. 'There is staff, of course, so we won't be completely alone.'

Keeping it staffed when no one was using it sounded like an alarming waste of money. And Kara could not help wondering whether he had brought his other PAs here—the ones he'd sacked on their return to England. Did he use it as a love nest? Had she been sucked in by his kindness? Was she right to be nervous?

She could not deny that the villa was enchanting, though. It looked like a fairy-tale castle, nestling into the hillside above the lake. But even so it did not make her feel any better about spending two whole days entirely alone with Blake—despite his assurance that whatever they did was up to her.

And it did not help when they were greeted by his army of employees, who looked at her as though she was someone very special. Too polite to do anything other than smile, she was relieved when they melted away after Blake had introduced her.

'They think that you and I are an item,' she whispered. 'I could see it in their eyes.' Blake had spoken in fluent Italian, while hers was non-existent, but they wouldn't have looked at her with such interest if they had known that she was really just his PA on a few days' holiday with her boss. No, they thought she was his girlfriend. She was sure of it.

Dark brows rose, hands waved airily. 'You are right. They probably are imagining that you are special since I have brought no one else here. But it is of no consequence. Do not let it worry you.'

At least he had assured her of one thing, and he sounded and looked more Italian than English at that moment, thought Kara. But it did little to alleviate her fears.

'Would you like me to show you around? Or perhaps you are tired and would prefer to rest?'

Resting sounded good—except that she would have felt safer in a hotel. If *safer* was the right word. Safer from what? From whom? Herself or Blake? She was afraid that she had been thrown in at the deep end. That this was not going to be the recreational break she had expected. For one reason because they were going to be totally alone, and for another because she was seeing Blake in an entirely different light!

Her feelings were running dangerously high. She felt an awareness that scared her rigid. She wanted to feel his arms around her, to feel the hard pulsing strength of him. Despite her misgivings, she wanted him to make love to her again. How could that be?

'I am a little tired,' she agreed. 'This is all so new and so—' She struggled to find the right words to say what was in her mind.

'Exciting?' he suggested, an eyebrow lifting, his body very still as he waited for her reply.

He was right—but perhaps not in the way he thought. What would he say if he knew how intense her emotions were? That she actually would welcome him holding her, maybe even kissing her, maybe even making love to her again? It was beyond sanity. She had never wanted a man even to touch her, and now she was craving it. One taste and she was hooked.

She drew in a deep breath. 'Different.' It hardly described her feelings—or maybe it did. Maybe it was the exact word. Every cell in her body was different. No longer calm and in control. They were dancing all over the place, hot and hungry for this handsome man.

It was strange that she was thinking of him now as more Italian. Had he truly changed or was it all in her mind? Was it this place?

'You never expected to find yourself here?' he questioned, his soft smile suggesting that he knew exactly how she was feeling. 'It is a shame that you do not want to stay longer. But perhaps after a couple of days spent in this very beautiful part of Italy you will change your mind? You will allow me to—'

Kara did not let him finish. 'No! I *must* go home, Blake.' Even saying the word *home* brought back the fears that awaited her there. She could not afford to let herself be distracted by him.

Something had happened to her here in Italy—something she dared not think about…something that needed to be crushed. There was no room in her life for romance—or whatever name she cared to put on what was happening to her now. No room at all.

'Kara—'

Quite how it happened she was not sure, but the next second she was being held against the rock-hardness of his chest, her head pressed into his shoulder, one strong, warm hand stroking her hair.

Blake could not bear to see Kara so agitated. He wanted to soothe away the fear he had seen in her eyes. Was it really because she was worried about leaving her mother, or did it go much deeper? Something to do with her father? Perhaps she had nightmares about him? Perhaps she was fearful that if she stayed too long she would give herself away in the middle of the night? Or was it being alone with him that she was afraid of?

He continued to murmur her name and smooth her hair against her nape until he felt her tension easing. 'No one is going to force you to stay against your will. Whenever you want to leave I will take you.'

She lifted her face to his, and when he saw tears in her lovely blue eyes he could not help himself. All his good intentions failed. This was a wounded woman and he wanted to make her better. His hand slid round to cup her chin and at the same time his mouth came down on hers.

What started as a gentle, reassuring kiss soon turned into something else. Into something fast and furious. Her lips parted on a sigh that suggested secret desire, and when he deepened the kiss, when he felt her response, when she kissed him back, he knew he could not resist.

Together they went upstairs, their mouths still clinging, and in his room he began to slowly undress her. In actual fact he would have liked to rip her clothes off and make love to her straight away, but he knew that to do so might make her fearful of him. And he did not want that. She had been fearful of her father. Once in a lifetime was enough to fear a person. He needed to be gentle.

As each inch of flesh was exposed he feathered it with kisses—and listened to her quiet moans of ecstasy. She tasted good, and her perfume made him even headier with desire. He would never have dreamed that his once prim PA could be so sensual, so sexy, so alluring.

Kara was aware of nothing except the fact that Blake's kisses, his touch, his energy, totally consumed her. They made love slowly and beautifully, over and over again. They did not surface, did not even stop to eat; food was the last thing on their minds. She had entered a world where nothing else mattered except the senses.

The touch of Blake's hands on her body. The excitement when he found that some parts of her were more responsive than others. The taste of his skin when she kissed him, when her lips dared to explore places that she had never let herself even think about before. The clean male smell when his body was so close to hers that they became one. The sight of him when he had just made love to her—his face both soft and raw at the same time, so different from the normally controlled man who had always scared her to death. And the sounds they both made when they were no longer in command of their bodies—grunts and groans, cries and shouts.

She knew that she would re-enter the real world soon, but she did not want to think about that. She was enjoying this new-found sexual liberation too much. She did not want it ever to end.

Even when Kara awoke the next morning she was still locked in her time bomb of happiness. She had learned so much from Blake. She had even instigated their lovemaking on one occasion. Her blood ran hot at the memory. What must he have thought?

'Kara?'

She suddenly realised that his eyes were open and he was watching her.

'Are you all right?'

'I—I feel—' *Embarrassed* was what she wanted to say, but the words would not come. How could she have behaved so wantonly? What had happened to her?

Blake finished the sentence for her, as he had on a previous occasion when she'd been stuck for words. 'Like a real woman? As though you've been on a voyage of discovery and found what you've been missing all these years?'

'I feel—different,' she confessed, her voice nothing more that a whisper.

He smiled. 'In a good way, I hope. You were magnificent.'

Magnificent! Oh, wow! Kara Redman, magnificent! They were words she had never expected to hear.

'And I don't know about you, Kara, but I'm hungry.'

Hungry? How could he think of food at a time like this?

'I'm going to jump in the shower. Care to join me?' And, before she could respond, 'Perhaps not. Or we'll never get any breakfast.'

He left the room without waiting for her answer and Kara pulled the sheets over her head. She had only to think of Blake's hands on her, stroking and teasing, his mouth nibbling and tasting, to feel swift arousal between her thighs and an almost insatiable urge to run after him.

It was crazy, it was totally insane, but she could not help herself, and she was still lying in the same position when Blake returned. He pulled the sheet aside and stood looking down at her. 'What are you doing, curled up under there?'

He looked magnificent, and completely unperturbed that he was as naked as the day he was born. Her eyes refused to move away from the muscled hardness of his chest, the damp curls of dark hair that arrowed down to narrow hips and— When she realised where her eyes were going Kara sat up with a stifled curse.

'I was waiting to use the bathroom.' And before she could give herself away she fled.

By the time she returned Blake was dressed in a white polo shirt and dark chinos, but his eyes were hungry as he looked at her wearing one of his cotton robes, tightly belted around her waist. She half expected him to make love to her again. But he didn't.

'I took the liberty of ordering a few clothes for you,' he said instead. 'I hope you don't mind, but I guessed you hadn't brought enough with you for a few extra days. Take a look in the wardrobe.'

Kara's mouth fell open when she saw dresses and skirts, tops and shorts—everything she could possibly need. 'You've bought these for me?'

'Yes.'

'I don't know what to say.' She was totally overwhelmed.

'You don't have to say anything, Kara.' All he wanted was to keep her here for as long as possible. She had turned into the most amazing lover. Ever since he had seen her transformation she had tortured his soul, but he had feared after last night that she might accuse him of simply bringing her here with the sole intention of seducing her.

But, no, she had been willing. At every opportunity he had given her the option to call a halt but she hadn't. Considering that she had never been with a man before, she responded to him with a passion that was both amazing and surprising. And definitely exciting. She had even pleasured him in a way that could only come from instincts as old as the age of man.

Two days with Kara would never be enough. He did not want full commitment; that was not what he was after. Not after what his ex-wife had done to him. As far as he was concerned there was no way of telling whether all women were the same, so it was far better not to let his heart get involved.

Besides, Kara would never bind herself to any man; she too had been badly hurt. But there was no reason why they could not indulge in an affair—maybe even a long-term one. She had shown that she was capable of enjoying intimate pleasures. Oh, yes, she had shown him in a very big way. A surprisingly big way! He had unleashed a tigress.

'I'll see you downstairs,' he said quietly. 'Otherwise I might be tempted to make love to you again.'

Kara felt colour flood her cheeks—especially when she saw the raw need in his eyes, which at one time would have scared her to death. Now it simply incited.

Once he had gone she dressed swiftly in a lilac cotton top and a lilac and white floral skirt—both of which fitted her perfectly. She marvelled that Blake had known her size. She brushed her hair and left it loose, and then hurried downstairs.

'You look beautiful,' were his first words. 'That colour matches your eyes. Did you know they are sometimes more violet than blue? Especially when we're making love,' he added with a knowing smile.

A swift tremor ran through Kara. She'd had no idea that her eyes were so expressive.

'And you should always wear your hair like that.' He threaded his fingers through it and pulled her face close. 'It suits you. You are a beautiful woman.'

With her heart racing she fearlessly met his eyes. It was amazing how much braver she felt now, so much more sure of herself. And even though her mind told her that she needed to be careful, her body took not the least bit of notice.

She had become a real woman, with all the needs and desires that went with it. No longer repressed, no longer hating all men. At least not this man! Not Blake. Blake had shown her that he was nothing like her father. He treated her with respect, with care, with gentleness.

Her eyes grew moist. Because she had never allowed any other man into her life she had never had the opportunity to judge for herself whether they were different. She had not even wanted to find out. She had judged herself of little value. Wasn't that what her father had told her, time and time again?

But now she knew differently. Blake would never have crossed the dividing line between business and pleasure if he had not found her attractive. And he would never have forced himself on her. After her initial paranoia she felt perfectly safe in his presence. She was not plain and worthless after all. She was beautiful and desirable. He had told her so.

'Kara, you are crying. Why?'

'I'm not,' she protested quickly. 'My eyes are watering, that's all.'

He smoothed a gentle thumb over her eyelids and then dropped a kiss on each one in turn. But he did not let her go. He kissed her on the lips instead, and all the fire and emotion that had burned so brightly last night came rushing back.

She was about to return his kiss, her arms already beginning to slide around him, when a woman's soft voice behind made her pull guiltily away.

'Breakfast is awaiting us,' he said.

The living area spread across the whole of the back of the villa, with floor-to-ceiling windows and sliding glass doors opening out onto a terrace dotted with plants in pretty coloured pots. It was there that their table was laid. Below was an arched entrance to landscaped gardens.

But it was the view that entranced Kara. The view over the lake. She could have stood there for hours, simply looking at it. The soaring mountains, boats, people, birds. Constantly something to look at, to take in, to capture in the memory of her mind. 'I wish I had my camera.'

'Maybe it's not the last time you'll come here.' Blake had been watching her, smiling at her pleasure, but now from behind he slid his arm around her waist and held her against him.

Kara chose to ignore his suggestion. 'It's certainly a beautiful location. Do you have a boat?'

'Naturally,' he said. 'And if it is your wish we will go out on it after breakfast.'

'Yes, please,' she said eagerly. 'I'd like that.' It was comforting being in his arms. Comforting and safe. Thanks to Blake, she was learning to trust. Considering that she had not wanted to join the conference in the first place she was now enjoying herself in a way that had been unimaginable a few days ago.

Blake was not the man she had imagined. She had always thought him to be a bit of a Lothario. And maybe he was. But at the moment he was treating her with delicacy and a genuine concern for her state of mind. He was allaying her fears, teaching her that everyone was not the same.

And it was working. *She* was not the same! She had become a different woman. She had felt a change in her in Milan, and even more so here, in this delightful part of Italy. How had he known that it would appeal to her? That it would bring out yet another side of her that she had not known existed?

He was changing her life, changing her views on life. And just for a few seconds she knew that she never wanted this period to end.

Breakfast was made up of an assortment of pastries washed down with cappuccino. Kara could not help thinking that if she lived here for any length of time she would become as round and plump as his housekeeper. Not that the cakes weren't delicious, but she was surprised that Blake had not asked for bacon and eggs.

Afterwards they explored the terraced gardens, and finally they reached the shores of the lake and a small cruiser moored there. Blake helped her into it, and she watched him as he started the engine, then untied the boat and guided it away from the shore. In everything he did he was confident and assured. She could not help but admire him.

Kara was silent to begin with, completely over-awed as they passed more magnificent shore-side villas. Dotting the tree-clad hillsides higher up were more modest houses, whole villages of them. And above them, above everything, the sky was the deepest blue she had ever seen, reflecting in the waters, which looked tempting enough to swim in.

'Everything's so beautiful,' she said on a sigh, her hands clasped in front of her as her eyes darted all over the place.

'Including you,' he said quietly.

For a brief second Kara remembered that Blake was her boss. But he was also her lover! Wasn't he? Her body grew suddenly hot at the thought, and she was unaware that her eyes were shining, that her cheeks had delicately flushed.

'Why have you always hidden yourself away behind plain clothes?'

The question was unexpected, and it surprised her. 'I think you know the answer to that.'

'Because of your father.' It was a statement, not a question. 'Why didn't you both leave him?' His head turned, his eyes locking into hers. 'Wouldn't it have been the wisest thing to do?'

'It sounds so easy, doesn't it? Just leave the monster

behind. But we couldn't. He— He—' Kara swallowed hard. 'He threatened us. I don't know what he would have done if we'd tried, but we felt that it was more than our life was worth. Not that our life was very good...'

Blake swore. 'It is a good job your father is dead, because I would personally—'

'Blake, please.' Kara put her hand on his arm. 'I should not have told you any of this. It's too private and too painful. Please, I don't want to talk about it any more.' Because if she did she would end up telling him about their money problems, and she knew she could not do that.

He closed his lips, but Kara could see that he was not comfortable keeping silent.

'That is why you tried to make yourself look like a nobody? To keep out of his way? You did not want him to know what a beautiful daughter he had. And it made you fearful of all men.'

Kara shrugged. 'Why don't you tell me about yourself instead?' she suggested, trying to inject lightness into her voice.

Dark brows rose. 'You mean you want *my* sad story? This was not intended to be a soul-baring mission. Today was supposed to be all about making you happy.'

'I am not unhappy,' she said immediately.

'But my insensitive questioning has brought back unhappy memories. I am sorry.'

He took her hand and pulled her against him, then draped his arm about her shoulders while he steered with his other hand. And when she looked up into his face he smiled and kissed her.

Instantly her problems were forgotten. Kissing Blake

was like turning on an electric lightbulb; it made her glow with energy. She knew that when they flew back to England all this would be over. Her life would return to normal. But she did not want to think about that now. She wanted to make the most of every moment.

They spent their whole morning exploring various inlets and promontories, stopping for lunch at a very beautiful hotel. Sometimes they were talking, sometimes sitting quietly watching other boaters, or the antics of water skiers in the distance, although Kara frequently found that Blake was watching her instead of the scenery.

The lake was much bigger than she had thought, and she could not help dreaming that one day she might be lucky enough to come back here and explore it all. 'You are very fortunate, having a villa in a place like this,' she said. 'And yet I have never known you take a holiday from work in all the time I've been working for you. Why is that? Why don't you use it?'

A shadow crossed Blake's face. 'I have secrets too, Kara. My memories of the villa are not entirely happy.'

He closed his eyes, and Kara could see that whatever the memory was it still haunted him. And if this was so why had he brought her here? She felt a cold shiver run down her spine.

'Perhaps we should not have come,' she said, unaware that her voice had changed, that she was emotionally pulling away from him.

'I wanted you to see it. I wanted to take pleasure from your enjoyment.'

'At the cost of yours?'

'I decided that it was time to let go of the past. I saw

someone who had been hurt as much as I had, but in an entirely different way, and I wanted to help. I hope I have done that?' Blake knew he was taking a big risk, talking like this, but it had felt right bringing Kara here, and now that he had seen the change in her he was glad that he had. But how did Kara feel? He held his breath as he waited for her answer. He was not usually so cautious when it came to his female acquaintances, and he absolutely never told them anything about his personal life. For some reason Kara had got beneath his skin. She was beginning to unleash her own demons too, and in the process revealing a side to her that he would never have guessed existed. She excited him in so many different ways.

She nodded slowly. 'I do feel a changed person here.'

'Then I have done what I set out to do, and helped myself in the process. You and I, Kara, although you may not believe it, are two of a kind.'

Kara shook her head. 'How can we be alike? Our lives are so very different, Blake! I can't imagine that there is anything similar about our lives at all.'

'Perhaps I do owe you an explanation,' Blake agreed after a few moments' thoughtful silence. But it was not going to be easy. Kara was the complete antithesis of his ex-wife. The two women could not be more different. Kara so innocent and honest; his wife two-timing and scheming.

He drew in a deep breath and let it out slowly, unaware that his unhappy memories were showing on his face. 'I was married once, a long time ago, to a woman called Melanie. When I married her I thought myself the luckiest guy in the world. She was blonde and beautiful and full of life. She enjoyed going out, socialising, parties—but I was busy building up my business. Nevertheless, I believed that I had got the balance right between work and pleasure.'

Kara waited, almost holding her breath. This was a side to Blake that she had never seen. A sad and sensitive side that she had not known existed.

Then his lips twisted wryly and a dark shadow crossed his face. 'Melanie, however, thought otherwise.'

He drew in a harsh breath and closed his eyes as memories flooded back.

'On holiday right here—a holiday she had insisted on taking, and one that started so happily, where she could not have been a more attentive and loving wife—she told me that she was pregnant. And, although I had not wanted to start a family so soon, I could not deny that the thought of being a father gave me great pleasure.'

He was silent for a moment and Kara could see the turmoil in his eyes, the wretchedness and the hurt, and she almost wished that they had not started this conversation.

Another sigh shifted through him, causing his eyes to grow hard and his jaw to tighten. Finally he spoke again. 'It was not until we got back to England that I discovered through a well-meaning friend that Melanie had been seeing another man. At first I was totally disbelieving, declaring that my wife would never do anything like that, but once the thought had been introduced into my mind I began to see that there could very well be some truth behind the accusation. Her behaviour was often erratic, and she would stay out much later than I had ever really noticed before. She would end phone calls as soon as I walked into a room, and she had started to spend a lot more money on seemingly quite trivial things. I knew I had to confront her and give her the opportunity to explain.'

Kara knew how hard it was for Blake to talk to her like this, and she was afraid to say anything for fear that he would close up and not finish his story. So she simply sat there looking at him, waiting, wondering.

'Initially she denied that she had been having an affair, and was angry with me for accusing her. I felt torn, but my suspicions would not go away, I knew by now that there was definitely *something* going on. Eventually, after another of her late-night parties, the truth came out. I think she had argued with her lover and was scared he might reveal her secret to me. Finally she broke down and told me that the baby was not mine but this other man's. Apparently he had told her he did not want to be a father, and once he had found out that she was pregnant had told her that their relationship was over.'

By the time Blake had finished his lips were grim and his eyes stone-hard. Kara almost wished that he hadn't told her. It was scary, seeing Blake like this. 'So she thought she would pass it off as yours?'

She felt for Blake. She felt his fury, his anger, his disappointment that his wife had cheated on him. And she wanted to throw herself into his arms and comfort him.

'I was so furiously angry. I could not believe that I had actually been sucked in by her lies. Her apologies afterwards meant nothing. I cast her out of my life and began divorce proceedings immediately. But it made me wary. I've trusted no woman since, and I'm definitely never going to get married again.'

'I'm sorry.' Kara did not know what else to say. What was there to say in the face of such duplicity? She did not know how Melanie had had the nerve to try and deceive him. She must have known that the truth would come out sometime.

'So you see,' he said finally, after a long silence when they were each deep in their own thoughts, 'we really are two of a kind.'

Never in a million years would she be like him, thought Kara. She did not have that hard edge that he hid behind. Her emotions came too easily to the surface. 'Have you seen her since?' She could not help asking the question.

'No. Nor do I want to,' he answered curtly. 'I'm sorry I've told you, I did not want anything to spoil our day.'

'I'm actually glad that you have,' she said softly.

'And I think it's about time we set off again.' He visibly shrugged off his mantle of discontent. Nevertheless he was silent for a while—until he found a secluded spot where he switched off the engine and tied up the cruiser. And Kara found out exactly what he had in mind when his dark gaze met hers, when she saw the searing hunger in his eyes.

'I need this, Kara. I've been wanting to do it all day.' His voice was no more than a low growl now, a growl deep in his throat, vibrating through her nerves, making her shiver with anticipation. At one time she would have felt fear if any man had approached her like this, but not so with Blake.

Although her body quivered her mind was open to him, and when his hands slid around her and she felt herself urged against his lean hardness, when she felt the full force of his arousal, hunger raced through her like quicksilver and there was no way on this earth that she could have resisted.

He had turned her into someone she did not recognise—and yet she did not hate herself for being weak. She could not. The pleasure was too intense. Simply being here and feeling the heated emotions spinning from one to the other was sufficient to capture her mind as well as her body.

Her eyes were on his mouth as it drew closer to hers, on his intensely sensual lips that could cause such devastating excitement. Unconsciously she touched her tongue to her own lips, moistening them in readiness, and she saw Blake's eyes narrow, the way he drew in his breath and became motionless.

What began as a gentle kiss grew swiftly into something hard and demanding. They each fed from the other, their bodies melding together as though this was where they rightly belonged.

Kara felt as if she was drowning in the waters of the lake, as if she was being swallowed up by the silky warmth that swam through her limbs and caused her head to spin. The mere taste of his lips was like an aphrodisiac, inciting her to return his kiss with a passion that both shocked and thrilled her.

Somewhere—somewhere in the back of her mind—rang a warning bell. Don't get into this too deeply, it said, or you might be sorry. But she did not listen. She liked what was happening. She wanted more of it. She was like a child who had been let loose in a sweet shop. She wanted to taste everything.

Heat gathered and swirled between her legs, her heart thundered, and when Blake took her hand and led her down to the cabin she made no demur. Urgently now, he stripped off his clothes, and Kara did the same. She felt no inhibition, though had anyone asked her a few days ago if she would strip off in front of a man she would have told them they had to be joking.

He feathered her skin with tiny kisses, causing her to buck and wriggle. Kara had never realised before how many sensitive areas she had. He was opening up a whole new world, and her enjoyment went beyond anything she had ever experienced.

It would be time to take a step backwards when they returned to London, when he would once again become her boss and she would be his perfect PA. There was no reason for her to believe that this would carry on. His affairs never did. But at least he had said that she would not be thrown out of her job. Not in so many words, but he had said that he never wanted to lose her—which amounted to the same thing, didn't it?

'I love the paleness of your skin,' he muttered, as his mouth moved from her breasts to trace a path over her stomach and towards his ultimate goal. 'Too many women think a tan makes them look healthier and more beautiful, but you are simply perfection.'

Kara loved the compliment he had paid her. And when his hungry mouth finally reached the soft whorls of hair at the apex of her thighs neither of them wanted to speak. The only sounds they made were of pleasure. The only movements they made were purely instinctive.

Kara could not believe how easily or how swiftly Blake brought her to her climax. It seemed that he had only just touched her and her world exploded. Again! As it had last night! What must he be thinking? It couldn't be very much fun for him.

'I'm sorry,' she said, her voice low and hoarse.

'Sorry?' he growled. 'Don't be. It's a compliment. Would you like to return the favour?'

What? Kiss him? There? Kara felt the blood rush to her face. He was asking too much. How could she? But within minutes she found herself teasing Blake in the same way as he had teased her. And whatever she was doing she must have been doing it right, because with the deepest groan she had ever heard he suddenly swung her onto her back and within seconds of protecting himself had entered her.

Kara lifted her hips to accommodate him and they both rode the storm together. She thought that she was going to black out, so intense was her pleasure, so many waves washing over her time and time again, and afterwards they both lay sated, unable to move, no strength left in their bodies.

Blake watched Kara, lying perfectly still with her eyes closed, and she lay there for so long that he wondered whether she was hating him now, whether he had overstepped the mark. There was a stillness about her that was scary. He felt sick to the bottom of his heart—until her eyelids fluttered open and she smiled. 'I think I have gone to heaven.'

Relief flooded through him. 'I was beginning to think that you thought badly of me.'

'How could I?' she asked, sitting up. 'I never knew that making love could be so beautiful. My mother always said—' She stopped abruptly and shook her head. 'Please forget I said that. I love my mother dearly. I would never say anything against her.'

Blake guessed that her mother's opinion on sex would have been based on the man she had married. The man who sounded like a complete monster. He forced himself to smile. 'We're not all the same. Myself and many other men besides me see women as objects of beauty, to be treated with respect and fairness. We would never demand anything they do not want to give. One day, Kara, you will find a man to love, and you will see that I am right.'

Kara felt as though he had just thrown her into the lake and left her to drown. He had just confirmed her suspicions that this was nothing more than a fling as far as he was concerned. A holiday romance! Something she would remember for the rest of her life but he would not.

How she managed to give the impression that there was nothing wrong she did not know. She glanced at her watch and pretended to be surprised at the time. 'We should be getting back.'

Despite what he had said, however, Kara still managed to feel total awareness, and she knew that if he wanted to make love to her again she would let him. He was in her bloodstream now; she could not get rid of him. He was a part of her and she was a part of him.

CHAPTER SIX

KARA and Blake had finished their dinner, and were seated outside on the terrace watching the sun slide slowly down behind one of the mountains. This surely had to be the most perfect place in the world, she thought, and felt sad that they had only one more day left.

She wondered whether she dared ask Blake if they could stay a little longer, but then remembered the fuss she had kicked up in the first place. And of course her mother would be expecting her! She suddenly sat up straight. How could she have forgotten her mother? How could she have spent a whole day without even thinking about her?

'Is something wrong?'

'I was thinking about my mother, wondering whether she's all right. I feel guilty now for—for enjoying myself.' *Enjoying* was too feeble a word to describe the emotions that had set her body on fire. It should have been something like seventh heaven or paradise, and she was glad that the darkening sky hid the hot colour that now flooded her cheeks.

'Then why don't you ring her?' And he tossed her his phone.

Even as he spoke her own phone rang, and as soon

as she heard the panic in her mother's voice Kara knew that something was wrong—very, very wrong—and she moved away so that Blake would not overhear.

'You need to come home,' said Lynne urgently. 'He's found out where I am. He was here just now, demanding money. I'm scared, Kara. He was really nasty. I've never seen him quite like that before.'

Kara felt her blood run cold. She had never heard her mother sound so worried. She was usually resigned to their lot in life. But she knew that she must not panic—even though she wanted to! She drew in a long breath and spoke as steadily as she could. 'Of course I'll come. Try not to worry. I'll speak to Blake. I'll be there as soon as I can.'

She spent a further few minutes trying to pacify her mother, who had a weak heart. Kara knew how dangerous it was for her to get worked up like this. And she needed to draw in a few more deep breaths herself before returning to Blake's side. Her heart was racing all over the place.

His dark eyes were questioning as he looked at her. 'Is something wrong? You've gone very pale.'

'My mother's not well. I need to go home.' She couldn't tell Blake the truth because it would to be embarrassing to admit to this man that her father had tricked them in such a blatant way. And, knowing Blake as she now did, he might want to do something about it. They would then be in his debt. And did she really want that?

The answer was a resounding no. Besides, once they got back to England their intimate relationship would be over. She was sure of it—convinced of it. He hadn't made her any promises. Far from it! Kara was certain that Blake wouldn't want to carry on their affair under the noses of his staff. No, a line would be drawn under the whole affair. It would be back to business as usual. Telling him about their debt would be a huge mistake!

She would need to treat these last few days as nothing more than a pleasant interlude. An overwhelming interlude! More than overwhelming, actually, but she could think of no other superlatives to describe what had happened to her. At least she would have memories. Totally amazing memories that she would hold for the rest of her life.

'I am sorry. Of course you must go.' Even as he spoke he was on the phone, and in what seemed like no time at all they were on their way to the airport.

The good thing about being with Blake was that he got things done, thought Kara. Money talked.

'What's happened to your mother?' he asked her now, genuine concern on his face. 'Is she in hospital?'

Kara shook her head, unaware that her eyes were shadowed and her face so drained of blood that she looked ill. 'She has a weak heart and amongst other things she suffers panic attacks—really bad ones. A legacy from my father, I'm afraid.' None of this was a lie; she was not making excuses to avoid the truth. 'She needs me. I should never have come away. I blame myself for this. I—'

'Kara!' Blake took her icy cold hands into his. 'You mustn't blame yourself. Everyone needs a break at some time. Perhaps you should get someone in to help with your mother? I'd be willing to—'

'No!' Kara almost shouted in her need to stop what

he was saying. Involving Blake in their family affairs was the last thing she wanted. Both she and her mother were too embarrassed by what they saw as their failings to want anyone to witness it—let alone the man who paid her wages!

If they had stood up to her father all those years ago, been brave enough to walk out on him, then none of this would have happened. But they hadn't, and now they were forced to face the consequences.

And the man they owed money to was becoming more and more demanding, more frightening with every visit. Kara was giving him practically every penny of her salary and it still wasn't enough. It was hard to believe that he had found out where her mother had gone.

If she hadn't thought her parent would be safe with Aunt Susan she would never have agreed to go to Italy in the first place. Even if it had cost her her job! The man had no conscience. He didn't care who he frightened so long as he had enough cash to fund his extravagant lifestyle.

During the flight Blake respected Kara's wish to remain silent, even though he didn't understand it. His attempts to talk to her had led to nothing, and he hated to see her so deeply troubled. He would be worried, too, if it was his mother, and he could understand her distress—but he did wish that she would let him in so that he could talk her fears through with her.

Instead she sat bolt upright, her eyes staring into space, her mind on whatever lay ahead. He would be there for her, he determined. He would give her any help she needed. If her mother needed hospital treatment then he would arrange it—pay for it, even.

Although he hadn't wanted it to happen, Kara had got through to him like no other woman ever had. He hadn't planned, didn't even want a permanent relationship, but something had happened. She had opened a tiny crack in his heart. And her pain was now his pain.

'Are you sure there is nothing I can do, Kara? I could phone ahead and arrange for—'

'*No!*' The word was immediate and loud, and then she said, 'I'm sorry. I didn't mean to snap. But I'm used to my mother's—attacks. She'll be all right once I'm there.'

'If you're sure? Because—'

'I'm sure,' she reiterated, her eyes flashing a vivid blue.

Blake felt sad at the loss of the beautiful woman he had found, the woman who had given herself so willingly. Who had transformed herself from someone plain and introverted into someone beautiful and outgoing. She had retreated back into her shell and he had no way of knowing what was going through her mind. 'If there is anything I can do,' he said again, 'you know you have only to ask.'

'I know.' Her voice was quiet once more. 'And, thank you, but we'll be all right.'

It was as though she didn't trust him, as though she wanted to compartmentalise the two sides of her life, and he could not understand why. He would have expected her to welcome his help after the time they had spent together, the closeness they had shared and enjoyed.

When the plane touched down he heard her on her phone, calling a taxi. 'Kara, please—let me take you. It will be so much easier. I have a car waiting.'

But she vehemently shook her head. 'I need to cope with this on my own, Blake.'

Kara saw the shock on his face but she had to do this. She did not want him knowing anything else about her private life. She refused even to think about the word *help*, as it brought with it feelings of both shame and hope.

When she got to her aunt's house and saw the state her mother was in she was glad that she had not let Blake bring her.

Her aunt Susan was all for them going to the police, but her mother was adamant. 'I'll be all right now Kara's home,' she kept saying. And when later that same day they returned to their own house she did indeed begin to look well again.

Kara knew that her mother was frightened, but she wondered whether part of her reaction was simply because Kara had not been around to rely on. An ache filled Kara's heart. For the first time ever she felt that she was being held back from a life that could be a whole lot better. She had experienced that life, had tasted a little bit of heaven—and unfortunately that was all it was ever going to be. One taste! A taste that would have to last her a lifetime.

Not that she'd truly expected anything more from Blake, but her brief experience of life on the other side meant that it would be hard going back.

Her mother, once she was settled and comfortable, naturally wanted to know all about her time spent away. And although Kara had no intention of telling her what had taken place between her and Blake, she could not hide the light in her eyes or the bloom to her skin as she spoke about her time in Italy.

'Tell me to mind my own business, but it looks to me as though something happened while you were there. You look as though you've fallen in love, Kara!'

In love! Bright colour flooded her cheeks even as she shook her head. 'I'm not in love, Mother. I'm never going to fall in love.'

'But something happened in Italy, didn't it?'

There was no hiding it. Kara shrugged, trying to give the impression that it was nothing. When actually it had meant everything to her. 'I did have a little romantic—liaison.'

Her parent smiled, suddenly looking happier than Kara had seen her in a long time. 'I knew it. Who is he? Are you going to see him again?'

Aware that her mother would not rest until she knew the truth, Kara drew in a deep sigh and let it go slowly. 'Actually, it was my boss.'

'Blake Benedict?' Shock registered on her mother's face. 'Was that wise, my darling? Doesn't he have a terrible reputation?'

'I guess.'

'And are you going to continue this affair?'

'Of course not,' Kara answered. 'I don't want the whole office knowing. It was just a—a holiday romance. A fling.'

Her mother looked at her wisely. 'You're not into flings, Kara. I hope he doesn't hurt you.'

'Blake won't do that,' she declared blithely. 'We've reached an understanding.'

At least she was assuming they had. They had not

actually talked about it, but she could not see Blake wanting to continue their affair now they were back in England. It had been exciting while it lasted—more than exciting. It had been an intense sexual experience. But she had resigned herself to the fact that that was all it was.

It was with trepidation, after spending the weekend at home, that she turned up for work on Monday morning. Blake looked both surprised and pleased to see her when she walked into his office.

'How is your mother?' were his first words. 'I wasn't sure that you'd be in today.'

'She's much better, thank you.' And *she* was all right too, now that she had seen him! One look into his face and she felt like a real woman again. What she would have liked was his arms around her, the strong, reassuring beat of his heart against hers.

'Are you sure?'

'Perfectly sure. Once we got home she was fine.'

'I didn't realise you were back in your own house or I would have come to see you. I had no idea where you were. I've been worried, Kara.'

'That's very kind of you, Mr Benedict.'

'*Mr Benedict?*' Dark brows shot up. 'What is this?' And then his face cleared. 'It's because we're at work, isn't it? You want to keep up appearances? Don't you think it might be a little difficult?'

'I wasn't even sure whether I still had a job. I know you said that you never wanted to lose me, but—'

'Kara!' Blake's eyes widened in astonishment. 'Whatever gave you that idea? I would be lost without you.'

For some reason she hadn't been able to help thinking

about the gossip that had flown around the office before her and Blake's trip to Italy. It had been common knowledge that his relationships with women were fleeting! Her thoughts must have shown on her face.

'Ah! Let me guess. You've heard that two of my previous PAs left after their respective conferences? And you, my innocent Kara, like everyone else, put two and two together and decided I'd bedded them and then dismissed them. The rumour amused me, but for your information it was the strain of working for me that they could not handle. Whereas you, my beautiful one, cope with *everything* admirably.'

Kara felt her usual blush coming on.

'And even in those dreadful clothes you are still sexy. I think I might struggle to keep my hands off you. You are both prim and desirable at the same time.'

'You flatter me, Mr Benedict.' She had gone back to her regulation dark suit, with flat-heeled shoes, her hair dragged back and her face bare of make-up. 'But what happened between us in Italy should be forgotten. I work for you, Mr Benedict. Let's leave it at that.' They were the hardest words Kara had ever had to say, but she truly believed that it would be for the best. 'Shall we start work?'

Continuing to see Blake would mean involving him in her family life, and that was something she did not want. She felt a very real need to keep her private and business lives totally separate.

Both his disbelief at what he was hearing and his displeasure that she was actually saying these words were very clear in his eyes. 'Can you really tell me, Kara, that you can stand there and look at me and feel nothing? Are you saying that even at this moment you do not feel a resurgence of the hunger we both felt?'

Kara sucked in a deep breath. 'Of course I feel it. But I choose to ignore it. And by so doing it will go away.'

'And if it doesn't?'

'Mr Benedict, you must realise that an office affair is not what I want. I should never have led you to believe that I would be OK with this kind of thing.' She felt extreme heat even saying those words. It curled around her stomach and made her feel ill. She had been fool-ish—very foolish. If word got out every person in every department in the building would know. She would be talked about. Speculation would be rife. There would be no getting away from it. She would be a laughing stock. Another gullible woman sucked in by the enigmatic Blake Benedict.

The idea made her stomach clench, and Kara knew already that she wouldn't be able to take being the centre of office gossip. She might even have to leave because of this foolish encounter with Blake! And if she left there would be no money to pay off… She let her thoughts go no further, they were far too disturbing.

His dark eyes met and held hers, and although she wanted to she could not look away. There was something mesmerising in them and she could actually feel herself being pulled back into that space she had inhabited for a few days. A few days of sheer unadulterated pleasure. A few days to last her the rest of her life!

'Will you do me the honour of dining with me to-night?'

Her heart quickened its beat and she took a step back, though still her eyes were locked into his. 'Have you not heard a word I've said? I cannot carry on an affair with you. Not right here under the noses of your staff.'

'So, our affair—it was all right while we were where no one knew you?'

'I lost my head,' she admitted. She had actually done more than that. She had lost her virginity. 'I let the magic of Italy carry me away. But I've come to my senses and—'

Her words were cut off when he swiftly closed the space between them and slid his arms around her. The next second his mouth was on hers and every sane thought fled. How could she fight when instant desire flared? When her body ignited? It was both crazy and beautiful at the same time.

It was not until he had thoroughly kissed her and was satisfied that she would no longer deny him what he wanted that Blake let her go. 'You lost your head in the most delightful way. You cannot deny that you want me—as much as I want you. I'll do my level best to keep my hands off while we're at work, though I cannot entirely promise. You're an incredible woman—do you know that? You're refreshingly different. Again I ask myself why I never noticed you before.'

'Because you go for glamour,' retorted Kara swiftly.

'Which I have now discovered can come in all sorts of guises,' he said on a groan. 'You may be dressed in the most conservative suit I've ever seen, you may not be wearing a scrap of make-up, but in my eyes, Kara, you are extremely beautiful. And I want you.' Even as he spoke, even as his voice turned low and throaty, his arms were tightening around her again, and his mouth claimed hers in a kiss that shot her into space.

Blake asked himself why he was doing this. Why he was persisting with Kara when she had told him quite clearly that their brief affair was over. Was it his wounded pride? Was he not used to women turning him down? Or had she really got beneath his skin in a way that no woman had since his marriage broke down?

He *had* actually intended ending their affair when they got back, feeling that he wasn't being fair to Kara, but found that he couldn't do it. More especially after her scare with her mother. She needed someone in her life—someone to care for *her*. Her mother was not the only one who had been traumatised by a beast of a man.

He had hardly slept the whole weekend for thinking about Kara, wondering how she was coping, wishing there was something that he could do. And when she'd turned up in one of her straitjacket business suits he had felt immensely disappointed. He had not expected her to come into the office, but he was glad that she had. Very glad!

The way that she dressed was in fact to his advantage. He did not want anyone else seeing what a stunning woman she really was. He would never get enough of her. Not that he wanted permanency, but contrarily he did not want to let her go. At least not for a long time yet!

'Am I being persuasive enough?' He deliberately kept his voice low and sexy as he posed the question. 'Isn't this what you want, Kara?' Because it was as sure as hell what *he* wanted. The merest touch of her lips against his fired a wild need through his body. Simply looking into her amazing blue eyes created a surge of adrenalin. There was no way he could work with her all day and not be allowed to release the energy she created. Kara had become a part of his life and he did not want to let her go.

'Mmm.'

It was the only sound he heard from her. Already he could feel her beginning to respond to him, the defences she had built so determinedly starting to crumble, and in little more than a few seconds her body arched involuntarily into his, her hips tight against him, her lips parting hungrily.

He should have felt guilty, but he didn't. Kara had turned into the most amazing woman—truly amazing— and he did not want to think that her strong virtues could hold him to ransom. He would not let them! He would do everything in his power to ensure she changed her mind.

Kara felt that she had let herself down. If she had not given herself to Blake in the first place then this would not be happening. She had become like every other one of his PAs—enchanted by Blake's seductive power.

He'd flattered her when he had probably seen very little that was beautiful about her. And she had responded to that flattery and given in to him. And why? Because she'd been available to him at the conference and he was too virile a man to go without sex for long. Colour flamed her cheeks and she tried to pull free.

To no avail. Blake's arms tightened resolutely. 'Do not think I'm unaware that your need is as great as mine.'

It was—but didn't he know that people would talk?

That her life would be hell if anyone found out she was being bedded by her boss? This was insanity of the highest order, and she ought to have known that from the beginning. What a crazy fool she had been to even *think* that Blake Benedict would settle for anything less than a full-blown affair.

'Kara…' His voice murmured softly against her mouth. 'It is all right. Everything is all right.'

No, it wasn't. It was all wrong. Everything she was doing was wrong. Except that another part of her mind, the insane part, was urging her to accept everything that Blake had to offer. He made her feel more feminine than she ever had in her life. He had given her a good feeling about her body. He had given her confidence. She had become a different woman, and if she was honest with herself then she truly liked that person.

But that was then and this was now. Circumstances were different. She could not go through with it. Except that there was still a part of her, a part of her head that was not connected to her brain, that was telling her it was all right to let go. That she deserved some pleasure in her life. That she could not remain a prim spinster because of the insecurity her father had beat into her, or because she needed to stay at home to help and protect her mother from the man who was ruling both their lives.

In the end she gave in to the primal urges that were taking over. She could no longer deny herself the excitement of being in Blake's arms, of his kisses, of his touch. Already an army of pleasure-seeking gremlins were marching through her body, tracking along nerves and veins, infiltrating her blood stream, resulting in her melting against him, accepting his kisses, returning them with a fervour that should have scared her but instead only increased her hunger.

When finally they both paused for breath, with Kara clinging on to Blake because she knew her legs would buckle if she let go, he said softly, 'My driver will pick you up at seven-thirty.'

'My mother—'

'I'm sure your mother will not mind you dining with me. Would you like me to talk to her?'

'No!' Kara's response was instant. 'I'll tell her myself.' Which meant that she had agreed to his suggestion—as he had known all along that she would.

She was not sure what her mother would say, though. Lynne had not been slow in voicing her opinion that the Blake Benedicts of this world did not take women seriously. Especially their personal assistants. And Kara really had no wish to heap any more trouble on their shoulders.

It was too late now to back out. She had given her answer by letting him kiss her. But when she got home at the end of the day, when she told her mother that she was dining with Blake, her parent's reaction was not what she expected.

'It sounds as though he is a good man after all,' she said. And when Kara came downstairs in one of the beautiful new dresses that Blake had bought for her, tears filled her mother's eyes.

Kara knew that she was thinking her father had been the reason why she had never worn fine clothes before. Her heart ached—both for herself and for her mother.

As she slipped into the waiting saloon Kara did not

see the other car parked on the opposite side of the road, or the driver watching her intently; nor was she aware that it pulled away and began to follow them.

Her head was in the clouds. Despite her own initial concerns she was excited to be dining out with Blake. Although she had been resolute in her decision today to let none of her time spent in Italy intrude, once Blake had kissed her every good intention had fled. And now she was filled with unbelievable anticipation.

As the city was left behind Kara began to wonder where they would be eating. The glass partition between her and the driver prevented her from asking, and it was not until he halted in front of a set of iron gates, passing through them as they opened to follow a long drive, that she finally realised she was being taken to Blake's home.

Pinpricks of excitement—or was it fear?—heated her skin, and she sat forward on the edge of her seat. But even though she was expecting something impressive nothing prepared her for the grandeur that confronted her eyes. It was a stunningly beautiful mock-Tudor-style house overlooking its own lake—not as large as Lake Como, but imposing all the same. And the house was quite simply huge, making Kara wonder how one man could live there alone.

He came out to greet her, casually elegant in pale grey linen trousers and a matching short-sleeved shirt. 'Welcome to my home.' He kissed her gently on the lips, and even that one light touch created a sizzle of excitement, and with his arm about her shoulders he led her inside.

Kara was totally speechless—even more so when

she saw the huge oak-panelled entrance hall. A staircase with barley-twist balustrades ran right up the centre, and she caught a glimpse of a galleried landing either side.

'I wasn't expecting this,' she said.

'Where did you think I lived? In some smart London apartment?'

'It would make more sense.' Surely this place was too big for him?

'I like space. I like the countryside. Quite simply I like it here. Besides, I do a lot of entertaining—corporate sometimes. It suits me perfectly. Would you like a tour, or are you hungry? I believe dinner is almost ready to be served.'

'Then we will eat first,' declared Kara, still breathless from both her impression of the house and Blake's nearness.

'Once again you look stunning,' he said, with something deep and throaty in his voice—something that sent a further quiver of hunger though Kara's veins. 'But no less sexy than you did today, in that terrible suit of yours.'

'How dare you call my suit terrible?' she said with pretended indignance, tossing her head, her thick glossy hair brushing the side of her face as she looked him straight in the eye.

His lips quirked. 'Of course—I was forgetting. It is your suit of armour. But unfortunately for you it doesn't work against me any more. You're ravishing, Miss Redman, whatever you wear.'

'Should you really be saying that to your personal

assistant?' she threw back, enjoying this teasing side to her employer.

'There are lots of things I'd like to say to you,' he growled, 'but none that would be appropriate for the moment. Perhaps later...'

The innuendo in his voice created a further chaotic river of excitement, and she could not help wondering whether he would suggest that she stay the night.

The dining room was as impressive as the entrance hall, with a polished oak floor and a beamed ceiling, and a long oak table in the centre that seated at least a dozen people. Laid for the two of them, it looked slightly incongruous. A bowl of sweetly scented pink roses freshly picked from the garden stood in the centre, with matching candles either side in silver candelabrum.

'You have gone to all this trouble for *me*?' she asked in an awed whisper.

'You do not think you are worth it? Come, let me prove that you are.' His kiss turned her hunger for food into hunger of a very different kind. And when his hands cupped the cheeks of her bottom, urging her against him, she was left in no doubt about his need of her too.

'Blake!'

'Mmm? Blake what?'

'We should not be doing this. We should be taking our seats. What if—?'

'Ahem!'

The sound of someone clearing their throat caused Kara to spring away. She felt one of her embarrassing guilty blushes coming on, but Blake was as calm and relaxed as if all they had been doing was talking.

'Ah, Mrs Beauman. This is Kara, and we are both absolutely starving. Kara—my housekeeper.'

'Pleased to meet you, Kara,' said the short, cheerful woman. 'Blake surprised me when he said he had invited a guest for dinner. I usually get more warning.'

'I hope I'm not inconveniencing you,' said Kara at once.

'Not at all.'

Kara waited until Mrs Beauman had left before she turned to face Blake. 'Well, that was embarrassing. I hope she knows I'm just your PA!'

'You are not my PA tonight, Kara. You are my— friend. My lady-friend. My—whatever you would like to call yourself. My lover, perhaps?'

Again that telltale blush, but more furiously this time. 'Please don't call me that, Blake. I know it's what I was in Italy, but things have changed.'

'Have they?'

'Of course they have. I keep you telling you that.'

'Except that your body tells me differently,' he said, his voice a deep growl in his throat. 'Don't try to hide or deny it. But let's not think about that now. Let's take our seats. Mrs Beauman does not like to be kept waiting.'

The meal was scrumptious. That was the only word Kara could use to describe it. Everything was home-made and tasty and tempting. They started with a very flavoursome carrot and coriander soup, followed by lamb chops with garden peas and new potatoes. Then fresh raspberries and cream for dessert.

There was nothing fancy about it, but everything was delicious. She ate too much, and drank too much, and by the time they had finished she was so relaxed that she was laughing and chattering as though Blake was a lifelong friend instead of the man she worked for.

Afterwards, instead of touring the house, they took a walk in the grounds. 'We need to walk our dinner off first,' said Blake, and Kara agreed. She was excited by the swimming pool, with its own changing rooms and sauna, but even more enthralled by the log cabin that stood in a lightly wooded area. It had a living room-cum-kitchen, a bedroom and a shower room, with decking at the front.

The house was lovely, but so big. This was cosy—this was something else. Intimate. Sexy. And clearly Blake thought so too. He caught her in his arms as they were viewing the bedroom and pulled her down on the bed. 'I've been wanting to do this all day,' he growled. 'You've been driving me insane, do you realise that?'

Kara had been determined not to let Blake make love to her tonight. If she let him get away with it now she would be for ever at his mercy. But what was a girl to do when her heart ruled her head? When her body craved fulfilment? When the most amazing man in the world, a man who could have any woman he liked, desired *her*? How could she refuse him?

CHAPTER SEVEN

'YOUR house is incredible.' Blake had just given Kara a guided indoor tour, and she had lost count of the number of rooms—each one furnished to an incredibly high standard. By comparison it made the house she and her mother lived in look like a doll's house.

'I will take that as a compliment.'

They were sitting in the conservatory, which looked out over the lake and the gardens beyond. The inky dark sky was laced with a myriad stars and a sliver of silver moon. The lake and surrounding area was lit by hidden lights. It reminded Kara of Lake Como.

'I still don't see why you want something so huge,' she said. 'Was it once your family home?'

Blake gave her one of his body-tingling smiles and shook his head. 'We didn't live anywhere this grand. My mother actually still lives in the house where I was born.'

Kara had seen a photograph of his mother standing proudly beside Blake at his graduation. She looked a very strong and very fine woman. 'And was that a photo of your father I saw in the drawing room?' She had meant to ask him at the time, but somehow their mouths had been otherwise engaged. She found it strange that he never talked about his father, though she supposed it was because he had lost him when he was so young.

Blake nodded. 'It was taken some years before he fell ill.'

'You look like him.'

'So I've been told.'

'What was he like?'

'He was very strict. He'd help me with my homework, make sure it was done, but he was of the old-fashioned school, believing that children should be seen and not heard. He was an academic, actually, his head always stuck in a book. He was kind and fair, though, and it was a sad day when he died. He'd been ill a long time and it was expected, but even so I wasn't too young to feel it.'

He went quiet for a moment, and Kara felt sorry that she had asked the question. She had not meant to bring back sad memories. If only her own father had been of such good character her life would have been so different. 'I expect your mother still misses him?'

He nodded. 'She does. She talks about him often. She has never found anyone else to love. I'll take you to meet her one day.'

Faint alarm filled Kara. Should she be flattered or worried? 'Won't she get the wrong impression? Won't she think there's something serious going on between us?'

'My mother knows I will never get married again.'

It was a clear statement of fact which put her firmly in her place, thought Kara. He had unmistakably confirmed what she had known all along. And even though her heart sank like a lead weight in a pond she tried to keep her tone light. It was all very well her surmising things, but to have them so clearly defined was not a happy feeling.

'She might think you've changed your mind,' she said, surprising herself with the lightness of her tone. 'Or do you take all your girlfriends to see her?'

'Certainly not! I've taken no one,' he declared—more forcefully, Kara thought, than was needed. 'There's no one I've wanted my mother to meet. However, you, my lovely Kara, are different. You may not believe this, but you might even be changing my mind about women! I'm beginning to believe that there are perhaps still one or two who are trustworthy.'

'I'm glad if I've restored your faith,' she said demurely. 'At least I've been of some service.'

'Some?'

The gleam of light in his eyes should have warned her. Despite his affirmation that he wished to remain single to the end of his days, she was still living on a high from their earlier lovemaking. It had taken on a whole new dimension. Felt different in the log cabin. She had given herself freely to him before, but there, in the woods, it had been as though they had taken a step back in time. As though they were the only man and woman on earth, and in their safe little place they could let go of everything. She would never have believed herself capable of being a temptress, of the things she had invited Blake to do, what *she* had done. Even thinking about it sent a fierce heat through every corner of her body.

'My beautiful Kara, *some* does not even begin to describe what you have done to me. Not only are you a sensational lover, but you do not have a bad bone in your body.'

'I do my best,' she said demurely, fluttering her eyelashes, fully aware that it would send his temperature soaring again. She was becoming a *femme fatale*, and actually quite liked the feeling of power it gave her.

His voice got slower and deeper and his eyes grew darker. 'I don't want this night to end—stay with me.'

'You know that's impossible.' She glanced at her watch and was horrified to see how late it was. 'I'm sorry, Blake. I must go,' she said, jumping to her feet. 'I didn't intend to stay this long.' She hated to admit it even to herself, but once again she had forgotten all about her poor mother.

'Of course. I'll drive you.' Blake had only drunk a small amount with their meal. Kara had wanted to keep a clear head too—especially as she was not used to drinking. Not that it had stopped her losing her head when Blake made love to her. His lovemaking was far more intoxicating than any amount of alcohol.

She knew that when she went to bed later she would relive every single action in minute detail. It was doubtful she would get any sleep. And yet he would expect her bright-eyed at the office first thing in the morning. Where she would have to act like she had never acted before. It was going to be hard hiding her emotions from the rest of the staff.

When they reached her house she turned to give Blake a quick peck on the cheek, but he was out of the car before her. 'I think it's about time I met this mother of yours, don't you?'

Swift alarm shot through her. 'She's probably in bed,'

she lied, knowing full well that her mother would be waiting up and wanting a full report on the evening.

'In which case I shall kiss you goodnight and leave. But it would be ungentlemanly not to see you safely indoors.' Even as he spoke his hand was on her elbow and he was walking her up the garden path.

Luck was not on her side. As soon as Kara opened the door her mother called out to her. 'Kara? Come and tell me all about your evening! I hope you didn't let that man—'

'Would "that man" be me, by any chance?' asked Blake, popping his head round the door that led straight off the tiny hall.

Kara wished the floor would open and swallow her up, but Blake simply looked amused and walked further into the room.

'Mrs Redman, I can assure you that I have taken very good care of your daughter. Let me introduce myself. I'm Blake Benedict, your extremely beautiful and extremely capable daughter's employer. She is worth her weight in gold to me. I would never jeopardise her future.'

Kara felt hot colour stealing over her neck and cheeks. He was going way over the top. But already Lynne was in his thrall, smiling up at him, completely oblivious to the fact that she was in her nightie. 'That is very reassuring to hear, Mr Benedict. I confess I was a little worried, but—'

'But now that you have met me your fears are allayed? It is good to hear. And, please—call me Blake. You are as charming as your daughter. I hope I shall see more of you in the future. But for now let me bid you goodnight.'

He took her hand and pressed a kiss to the back of it, and when Kara walked with him to the front door she said, 'Thank you for being so kind to my mother.'

'I imagine she has had little attention paid to her over the years, so the pleasure is all mine.' He tilted her chin with his fingers and kissed her gently. 'Thank you for this evening. And if you're late in the morning I shall understand why.'

'I shall not be late,' she told him quietly. Whatever was happening between them, she still intended to do her job properly.

As Blake drove home he found himself humming an old love song, and alarm bells rang in his head. Surely he wasn't falling in love with Kara? Surely not? She was beautiful and exciting, and he enjoyed being with her, making love to her. She was refreshingly different. But that was all it was—wasn't it? Enjoyment? He was not looking for a long-term relationship. Commitment. Hell, no! Once was enough. He was done with that sort of thing. Love and marriage was definitely off his agenda. He intended remaining single to the end of his days.

He had meant what he said when he'd told her that she was helping him to change his mind about women, but it still did not mean that he wanted to get serious.

Happy now that he had convinced himself he was in no danger, Blake did not even notice that he had begun humming the love song again—and in the weeks that followed he did not question his actions. As far as he was concerned they were indulging in an affair which would one day end with no regrets on either side.

It stunned him, therefore, when he turned the corner to her road one day, ready to pick her up because he had planned a lavish dinner with a show to follow, to see her in the arms of another man.

At first he could not believe his eyes. Something harsh and sharp ripped through him and his first instinct was to confront them. But even as he watched the man let her go and turned and disappeared, while Kara hurried into the house.

Blake sat there for a few minutes, trying to reconcile himself to what he had seen.

When he finally picked her up she said nothing. She did not even look guilty. He began to wonder whether he had read the scene correctly.

He needed to ask. He knew that if he didn't it would fester in his mind. 'Who was that man I saw you with?'

Kara frowned. 'What man?'

'Outside just now, when I turned the corner.'

'Oh, you saw him?' The words popped out before she could stop herself, and she felt the blood drain from her face. 'He was no one.' But her heart did a painful drumbeat. How she wished that he was no one. How she wished that he wasn't their worst nightmare.

'No one? When he had his arms about you?'

Kara shivered. Blake looked so cold and condemning that she was suddenly afraid. 'He came to see my mother. He was saying goodbye, that's all.'

She wished that she could tell him about the loan shark, but it was such a deep stigma—so horribly embarrassing and shameful. It was something she and her mother had to deal with themselves. And now the unpleasant man had unfortunately seen her with Blake, realised she had a wealthy boyfriend, and was upping the interest on the loan again.

Blake's brows lifted. 'It was a funny goodbye. It looked as though he was kissing you.'

Spitting fury into her face was more like it. He had shoved his nose right up to hers and she had been scared to death. He had never been quite this aggressive before. 'It was just a peck on the cheek,' she said, mentally crossing her fingers that he would believe her.

Finally he relaxed. 'You had me worried, Kara. I thought I had competition.'

'There is no one else I'd rather be with,' she said, smiling gently and touching the tips of her fingers to his face. She actually felt as guilty, as if she *had* been two-timing him, and it was hard to control a tremor.

He took her hand and pressed a kiss into its palm before giving it back to her. 'Let's enjoy our evening out.'

Kara did enjoy her evening, but she could not forget the close shave she'd had and wondered whether she ought to stop Blake coming to pick her up. She had no idea how it had started, because he had always used to send his driver. But lately he had come for her himself, and he always made it his business to have a few words with her mother.

Lynne thought he was amazing. She thought him a good man, and good for her daughter, and had expressed the opinion that they might have a future together.

'You're being silly, Mum. Blake's not the settling down type. One marriage was enough for him.'

'Then why are you wasting your time with him if there is no future in it?'

'It's not a waste,' answered Kara. 'I'm experiencing life.' She wasn't going to tell her mother—not yet, at least—that she thought the signs were hopeful. Blake had only the other day begun to talk about something they might do in the future. And if that didn't mean he was serious then she did not know what did.

But life had a way of kicking her in the face when she was least expecting it, and of making niggling fear become reality.

CHAPTER EIGHT

KARA stared at the tiny window, refusing to believe her eyes. This was not right. It could not be a true reading. But it was. She was deluding herself. It did not lie. She had known without the test. It had merely confirmed her fears. She slumped down on the edge of the bed, suddenly feeling icy cold. She was pregnant.

How it had happened she had no idea; Blake had always been so careful. Her out-of-control heartbeat echoed so loud in her ears that it was deafening. A baby! A baby who would take time and money. How could she clothe and feed a baby when already almost every penny of what she earned went towards paying off their debts?

Please, God, don't let this be real, she prayed. Don't let this be happening. But the truth was there in front of her. Nothing could be more real.

Blake would not want to be lumbered with a child— hadn't he told her he had no intention of playing happy families? She could imagine his disbelief when she did confess. He might even blame her. Wasn't that what men did? Some men anyway, at least.

He might even suggest paying for a termination, although she really had no idea what his thoughts on the matter were. Even thinking about it was enough to fill her with horror. Then she shook her head. No, he wouldn't want that—and neither would she, no matter how hard things got.

What she really ought to be thinking about was how she was going to cope. Once she had to leave work she could see no way out of their financial difficulties except to move away—somewhere the loan shark wouldn't find them. Otherwise how could she provide for a baby when he was sucking all their money from them?

Tears raced down her cheeks as she sat there looking at the evidence, willing it to change. But no power on earth could do that. She had to face the fact that she was to become a mother, with all the complications that involved.

How could she tell her own mother, even? How could she admit that she had got them into deeper trouble? The future looked bleak. Even if they moved and escaped the claws of the money-lender they had no savings to fall back on. It didn't look well for the future.

She waited until that Friday to tell Blake the news. It had become a habit for her to go to his house for dinner. He invariably tried to persuade her to stay the weekend but she never did, insisting that she could not leave her parent. Always, but always, they ended up in bed, and it would be very late when she got home.

This evening Kara felt nervous, and began toying with her food. Blake was not going to be happy; that was a certain fact. She felt sure that he did not see her as a permanent fixture in his life. Ought she to get out of here now and say nothing? Except that a few months down the line he would notice anyway. There would be no hiding the fact that she was pregnant.

'Is something wrong?' A faint frown grooved Blake's brow and his eyes were full of concern. 'You've been chasing that piece of chicken around your plate for the last five minutes. Are you not feeling well?' He reached his hand across the table to touch hers. 'You've looked a little pale all week. Do you think you're coming down with something?'

Finally Kara looked at him and made herself smile, ignoring the butterflies that were creating havoc in her stomach, trying to look as natural and joyful as possible. Perhaps if she looked happy he would be happy. 'I have some news for you.'

His brows rose. 'Go ahead.' He smiled expectantly.

It was now or never. 'I'm—pregnant, Blake.' There was no other way she could say it. No way to cushion the blow. 'I'm having your baby.'

But he didn't look happy. She had been hoping for too much. His expression was one of total disbelief and his eyes fixed firmly on her face, making her shiver inside. 'You cannot be.'

'I think I should know whether I'm pregnant or not,' she said, trying her hardest to ignore his reaction. It was a shock for him, the same as it had been for her. He needed a few minutes to let it sink in. She prayed this was the case. 'I'm definitely having your child, Blake.'

Her heart stopped beating as she waited for his response, and she did not like what she saw. A frown drew his brows together in a hard, straight line, narrowing his eyes, turning them into silver slits, and he looked at her as though she was a complete stranger telling him something he did not want to hear. There was none of the compassion and warmth that had been there a few seconds ago. Nothing but stone-cold disbelief.

'Tell me this isn't true.' His whole body was taut, every muscle clenched, his eyes silver and dangerous.

Her stomach began to churn uncomfortably. It was almost as though he was saying that he did not want their child. Which would be the cruellest thing in the world. Too cruel even to contemplate. She knew that he'd been hurt in the past, cheated on by his wife, but even so...

'I've done a test,' she said, quietly but firmly, keeping her eyes level on his despite the churning of her stomach. 'I'm definitely pregnant.'

Kara heard the breath hiss out of Blake's body as he turned away to look out of the window. She saw the tenseness in his shoulders and knew that she had to say something to defuse the situation. It was going to take him time to get his head round it. But the fact remained that she was carrying his child, and there was nothing either of them could do to change it.

'Are you certain that it's mine?'

Before she could answer he turned around, and Kara was shocked by the light blazing from his eyes. 'Of course I am.' Her jaw dropped and she stared at him in disbelief. 'How can you even suggest that I might have been with someone else? You have taught me everything I know about relationships, about trust, about making love.'

'Love?' He tossed the word into the air as though it did not exist. 'I don't believe in love—not any more. We had sex—very good sex.'

Although Kara knew where he was coming from, his harsh words still hurt. 'I'm not like Melanie, Blake.' She kept her voice soft and calm—just about. It was difficult in the face of such opposition. 'I can promise you I've been with no other man.'

'I saw you in the arms of someone else.'

His eyes had taken on a scary sheen and she shivered inside. 'And I told you who he was. Why would I want any other man when I have you?' It was hard to believe that he thought she was capable of going behind his back. She was not like his ex-wife; she would never, ever do anything underhand. Surely he knew that? Surely he knew her well enough by now?

She felt as though her whole world—her new and beautiful world—was crumbling at her feet stone by stone. Everything they had built up together being destroyed because he couldn't accept that she was pregnant with his child. Did he think she was happy about it?

It was a struggle even to breathe. Had it been his intention all along to have fun at her expense and then drop her as he had all the other women in his life? And now that she had announced she was pregnant it had put a whole different complexion on things.

Blake had taught her more about herself than she would ever have discovered if she had not been with him. He had made her believe in herself. She had finally become a confident woman. And now he was throwing it all back in her face. Her father had been right. She was a worthless creature. She had sold her body—and for what? The only way now was downhill.

Her tears finally came, and she swung away so that he would not see. She did not want him accusing her of turning them on so that he would take pity on her. Pity was the last thing she needed. What she wanted was for him to accept that they were having a baby. She wanted him to comfort her and assure her that he would look after her. She needed him. She did not want to go through this alone.

Blake's mind was in turmoil. He did not want children. Love and marriage and the whole happy family thing was not for him. He'd tried marriage once and it hadn't worked. He did not want to do it again. He had sworn he would never do it again.

He closed his eyes. Something had gone terribly wrong and he needed time to think about it. His whole world was spinning out of control and he was clinging on for dear life. It was hard to get his head round what Kara had just told him. He wanted to be alone.

'We will talk about this again later,' he said, trying to remain calm while inside a wild storm was raging. 'It would be best if you left now.' He spoke into his mobile, and seconds later Kara was being driven away.

The hurt in her eyes remained with him.

Drawing in a deep breath, trying to wipe the picture from his mind, Blake poured himself a large glass of whisky and sat down. He would be a very pathetic individual if he did not accept that Kara was telling the truth. She was so very different from any other woman he had gone out with. And nothing at all like Melanie. And yet he had questioned whether the baby was his.

It had been a gut reaction. The very thought of being a father scared him rigid. His mother had told him, some years after his father's death, that she would have liked more children, but her husband had been dead set against it. He'd actually not wanted Blake in the first place, although he had loved him once he was born.

And, since Blake was never happier than when he was working, he often felt that he was following in his father's footsteps. But if it was true and Kara *was* expecting his baby then everything would change. This did not make him feel happy. He needed time to think.

He had been thrown by the dramatic change in Kara in Milan; she had gone to his head. She had turned into a beautiful woman almost overnight—a beautiful, sexy woman who had welcomed her own femininity, who had been startled by it but had grown with it. He had watched her develop and mature and take pride in her sensuality, and he had felt something grow within himself too.

And now, in an instant, whatever it was that had been developing inside him—whether it was love or infatuation of some kind—had dealt him a body-blow. He hated himself for doubting Kara, for questioning her relationship with the man he had seen her with. And he blamed Melanie for making him wary.

Or was it his own take on the whole baby thing that was refusing to let him accept that he was about to become a father?

A few whiskies later, he was still thinking about his problem.

Kara wished that she had stuck to her guns and not gone to Milan—then none of this would have happened. And if she had not weakened it would not have happened either.

Life was cruel. It had been hard when her father

was alive, and even afterwards with the debts he had left them, but this was worse! Having Blake believe, if only briefly, that she would trick him into thinking that another man's baby was his had created the deepest, darkest fear she had ever experienced.

Even when her father had hit her she had not felt like this. She had cowered away and run to hide, but she had not felt as though her world was coming to an end. There had been a sort of inevitability about it—as though somehow it was all her fault and she deserved it.

But she did not deserve *this*!

The moment Kara walked into the house her mother asked her what was wrong. She thought of saying nothing, but her parent was not stupid and she would have to know the truth sooner or later. There were most likely still traces of tears on her face even though she had done her best to dab them dry.

'I think my relationship with Blake is over.'

Lynne said nothing, wisely waiting for her daughter to explain.

But seeing the sympathy on her mother's face caused her to lose what frail hold she had on her composure. Tears filled her eyes and rolled down her cheeks. 'He sent me home.'

Her mother still remained silent, holding out her arms instead. Kara walked into them, feeling like a child once again, when her mother's kisses had always made things better. Not that they would this time. Nothing could make her feel better.

'I'm pregnant, Mum, with his baby, and he's not happy about it.'

This did have her mother snapping to attention. 'You're pregnant?' And her eyes, so very much like Kara's, though their intense blue had faded over the years, widened in dismayed surprise.

Kara nodded, her misery mirrored in her expression. 'Whatever you do, don't censure me. I did not mean it to happen. We've always been careful. I don't know how it happened, but it has.'

Lynne stroked her daughter's hair and looked sadly into her face. 'I won't confess I'm not shocked, but it's not the end of the world, my darling. Blake must be in an equal state of shock. He'll need time to get over it. But he'll come round, you'll see. He's a good man.'

'I wish I could be as sure as you.'

'Men are strange creatures—you should know that,' said her mother. 'Look at your father.'

Kara did not even want to think about her father. 'I thought Blake was different.' She moved away, walking to the other side of the room. 'He's the only man I've ever felt comfortable with, the only one I've ever trusted. He brought me to life. He made me feel good about myself. But he's no different to the rest, Mum, when it comes down to it.'

Her mother's eyes widened again. 'I'm sure that's not true. It's my guess that in a few days' time he'll accept the inevitable. He cannot turn his back on you—not when he's the father.'

'He even questioned whether he was the father.' She might as well tell her the whole truth.

Lynne's brows drew together in a deeply disbelieving frown. 'But if you're not out with him you're always home. Why would he think that?'

'He did see me with someone,' she admitted, with a wry twist to her lips.

Confusion clouded her eyes. 'Who? A work colleague?'

Kara shook her head and remained silent, but her mother would not let it go. 'Then who?'

'The loan shark.'

'The loan shark?'

'Yes. Outside the house one evening. He was threatening me. I didn't tell you because I didn't want to alarm you. Blake saw him from a distance and thought we were kissing. I—*Mum!*' She lurched forward as she saw her parent slump in her chair.

What followed afterwards was like a nightmare. The ambulance. The hospital. The waiting. Kara blamed herself. She should never have mentioned that horrible man. He was her mother's worst enemy. Pure evil. The bane of their lives.

She spent all night at the hospital, worrying herself sick, feeling better only when her mother was declared out of danger. A suspected heart attack was ruled out, but Kara was told that her mother needed to rest and be kept calm. Because of her weak heart an attack in the future was not an impossibility.

A day later Lynne was allowed home. She looked pale and needed to rest, but insisted that Kara did not take any time off work. 'I'll be all right. If you don't go Blake will think you're staying away because of him—because you're scared.'

'Of Blake? Never!' she declared fiercely. She was more fearful for her mother's state of health. Nevertheless her parent was right. She did need to go. Neither of them mentioned the crook who was after their money, but Kara watched her parent sometimes sinking deep into her own thoughts, while her own were all over the place. She wished over and over that she had not brought him into the conversation. It made her more aware than ever of the effect the whole thing was having on her mother. How were they ever going to manage when the baby came along? Kara's hopes for the future were very bleak.

She arranged for a neighbour to sit with her mother while she went to work on Monday, and it was a relief to discover that Blake was absent—although she knew that he had been in earlier because he had left her a whole list of instructions. Her heart—which had been dancing all over the place at the thought of coming face to face with him again—quickly settled into its usual rhythm.

It was almost the end of the day before he returned, and when he did he called her in to his office. Kara kept her chin high and her eyes brave, even though her pulses were racing.

'Sit down,' he said roughly, when she remained standing in front of his desk.

Kara sat. Glad to do so because her legs were in danger of collapsing beneath her. There was something about Blake's expression that sent ice slithering down her spine. A few short weeks ago, even a week ago, she would never have imagined that their relationship would be put in jeopardy. She was the happiest she had ever been. And now she had no idea what her future held.

CHAPTER NINE

'I CANNOT say in all truthfulness that I am happy about this situation, Kara,' said Blake, his eyes a light, telling silver.

'And you think I am?' she asked, hearing the sharpness in her voice but unable to do anything about it.

'We were both in shock the other day. I perhaps said things I should not have done.'

He could say that again! She did not like her honesty being questioned.

'We need to talk. Will you come home with me tonight so that we can discuss this matter over dinner?'

This matter! He made it sound like a business deal. And the way she was feeling at this moment she did not want to join him for dinner, tonight or any night. It was spending so much time with him that had got her into this mess. 'I don't see why we can't talk here and now.'

A frown dragged his brows together. 'It's hardly conducive.'

'To what? Intimacy?' Oh, God—why had she said that? Why had she even thought it? Except that intimacy was what they experienced every time she went to his house. Nevertheless she went on bravely. 'Have you any idea how much this is going to change my life, Blake?'

'I've thought of nothing else.'

'Is that so?' Still Kara couldn't keep the irony out of her voice. 'Or were you perhaps thinking more of yourself? The way it will change *your* life? Your single life. Your free and easy life. Because, believe me, I'm not going to bring this child up on my own. You're the father and you're going to play a part too.' How brave her words sounded—not that she was feeling brave. Anything but.

'I would not want it any other way' he said. 'I may not have planned on this child, Kara, I freely admit that. It has stunned and shocked me, but I *will* be involved in its upbringing.'

What exactly did that mean? Be involved? On what basis? A part-time father? Or would he do the honourable thing and suggest marriage? Her heart raced at the thought of being married to Blake. Suddenly she could think of nothing she would like better than to be married to Blake, to go to bed in his arms every night and to share her deepest fears over the future. Being Blake's wife would be the perfect solution to this problem, but Blake had said he would never marry again. And she had no idea what was in his mind now.

She already knew his views on marriage, but now there was a child involved—*his* child. Did he believe in a child having two parents who were tied together by marriage? Or was he a modern man who believed that marriage was not necessary to raise a baby? She did not doubt that he would provide for her and the baby, but how about personal support? Would she get that?

Would he want her to live with him? Or would his support come in the form of financial security? There was so much they had to talk about.

'I'm not trying to get out of anything, Kara, but I need to know your plans.'

'I've not had time yet to make any,' she threw back crisply.

'It has come as a great shock to both of us,' he agreed. 'I will obviously get you the best medical attention possible. I will personally—'

Kara held up her hand and shook her head at the same time. 'Don't think that throwing your money at this is the answer, Blake. What would have been nice was your belief in me. Have you any idea how much it hurt when you questioned whether the baby was yours? I guess I was stupid, naive. You didn't want anything long-term from me. You're simply after yet another affair. I'm just one in a long line.'

How she managed to speak without breaking down Kara had no idea, but she was not going to give Blake the pleasure of knowing how much he had upset her. Anger was her best form of defence.

'That is not the case.'

'What? I'm *not* one in a long line?' His affairs were common knowledge in the office. Everyone knew what he was like.

Blake shrugged. 'I admit I have had girlfriends. You already know that. But you are different.'

'And isn't that what you say to them all?' Her words came hot and fast, and she didn't care. Her whole world was crumbling about her feet. It had been bad enough when her father was alive, but now it was a thousand times worse. What she needed, what she really wanted, she suddenly realised, was his instant reassurance that this baby would bring them even closer together. She could do without the whole marriage thing, but she could not do without Blake. She knew now that she had fallen in love with him. He had made her feel wanted and special and free for the first time in her life, but his attitude now was causing her nothing but heartache.

'Such a question does not deserve an answer, Kara.' His jaw tensed, muscles working in his cheeks as he strove to keep a hold on his temper.

Perhaps it had been below the belt. But she was angry. Damned angry. She felt that it was only grudgingly that he was offering her the support she needed, for duty's sake. She and the baby were a mistake that Blake wanted cleared up. She would have to take his help, of course— she would be a fool not to—but, oh, how she longed for him to have offered it straight from his heart.

'The first thing we need to do is make a doctor's appointment to get your condition confirmed.'

'I don't need it to be confirmed, Blake.' She kept her eyes steady on his, challenging him.

'But you still need to see a doctor. I wish to take care of you.'

He wished! Kara wished that she had never gone to Italy with him. It was turning out to be the biggest mistake she had ever made! What a fool to fall in love with her boss—a man who clearly had a heart of stone. It was the worst thing she had ever done. But he was throwing her a lifeline, and she would be an even bigger fool to turn it down. 'Very well,' she answered reluctantly.

'Do you want to take some time off work?'

He was being so damned practical! All she wanted was his love! But that was an empty dream now. It would never happen. He was doing what he was doing because it was the right thing. 'I would appreciate a few days. My mother's not well. She's been in hospital.' She would love to tell him the reason why, but their relationship was clearly over. She would never share those secrets with Blake now.

'Why didn't you say?' he asked at once, his eyes sharp with surprise. 'You should not have come in under those circumstances.'

'And have you thinking that I was being a coward? Not a chance, Blake.' She saw the way his nostrils dilated, the flare in his eyes quickly disguised, and felt a grim sort of pleasure.

'I'll drive you home,' he said. 'You should be with her.'

Kara's chin tilted. 'There's no need. I have my car.'

It was not until she'd left his office that Kara realised how badly she needed to breathe. She drew in deep lungfuls of air, closing her eyes and holding on to the edge of her desk as she felt her world swing on its axis. She did not see Blake follow her. Knew nothing until she felt an arm about her waist, her head pulled down on his shoulder.

'I'm taking you home,' he said firmly. 'No arguments. You're in no fit state to get behind the wheel.'

Thanks to you, she thought, wanting to pull free but unable to stop herself responding to his touch. Crazily, in spite of everything, she wanted to relax and let him take care of her. She wanted his strength to be her strength. It would be so easy. And yet so dangerous!

She sat silently beside him in the back of the car, hardly conscious of him issuing instructions to his driver. It was not until they reached her house, when Blake jumped out and made to walk up the path, that she spoke. 'There's no need for you to see me in. I'm—'

'I believe there is,' he said sharply. 'Besides, I'd like to see your mother. To a degree I feel at fault. If there is anything I can do to help, then—'

'We don't need your help, Blake,' she said with fierce determination, wanting to tell him the whole truth, confess the desperate situation they were in, but knowing it would do her no good. 'All we want—all I want is to get on with my life.'

Blake's eyes sparked determination. 'You're forgetting that I am a part of your life now.'

And trying to stop Blake when he had set his mind on something was like trying to hold a London double-decker bus up in the air single-handedly.

Lynne's face was a picture when Blake followed Kara into the house. 'Mrs Redman,' he said immediately. 'Kara tells me you've been in hospital. I trust you're feeling better?'

Kara saw the surprise on her mother's face and spoke quickly. 'Blake says that I can take a few days off to look after you. Isn't that good of him?'

Her parent looked from her to Blake and then back again. 'Yes, it is. Thank you, Blake.' But her words were stilted, and Kara knew that she did not mean them.

'It is my pleasure,' he answered.

'I will take the rest of this week off, if that's all right,' said Kara quickly, anxious to get rid of him, out of her house and her life, so she could start the difficult task of moving on and getting over him—as if that would ever be possible! 'But I will be at my desk first thing on Monday morning.'

Kara did not realise quite how tense she was until he had left, then she sank down on a chair and closed her eyes. But she soon snapped them open again when her mother spoke.

'What have you told him?'

'Nothing. Just that you've been in hospital. He didn't ask why and I didn't volunteer anything. You don't really think I'd tell him about our money troubles?'

Lynne closed her eyes, and she was silent for so long that Kara began to feel worried. 'Mum?'

'Blake's a good man, you know,' Lynne said, looking at her daughter now.

Kara sighed. 'I know. He's promised to help, but I have a feeling that deep down inside he hates me now. I just know it. Me and this baby are going to be a complication in his life and he doesn't like it. Oh, Mum, everything was going so well between us. I really thought my whole life was going to change. I've been such a fool.'

'You have been no such thing, Kara,' said Lynne, pulling her daughter into her arms. 'Blake just needs time to get used to the idea of the baby.'

During the week that followed Kara tried to push Blake out of her mind—except that it was virtually impossible. The practical half of her hated him. The other half, the sentimental half, grieved that she might never see him again, might never be held in his arms or share his bed again. He had taught her what love was all about and she had embraced it with both arms—and now they were empty, and destined to remain that way.

The only person she would have to love would be her baby. Blake's baby! The baby he didn't want! He was going to take care of her welfare during her pregnancy, and hopefully later he would want to play a part in the baby's life. But as far as she could see it would only be duty that kept him close. Commitment and marriage were anathema to him.

She'd half expected him to pay them a visit, or at least telephone to say that he had made her an appointment with a doctor, but she heard nothing. A whole week of nothing. And although her mother's health improved, her own temper did not.

It was not until she arrived for work on Monday morning that Kara found out why he had not been in touch—and her heartbeat accelerated to such a degree that she felt sure it was not good for her.

Blake had been involved in a car accident a week earlier. He hadn't been in the office since, and was now convalescing at home.

A week ago! The day he had left her house!

Kara's heart went cold. Why hadn't he told her? Wasn't he well enough? Or did he think she had worries enough? Maybe she ought to go and see him? Or telephone him at least?

She was kept busy all day, but as soon as she got home she rang him. 'Blake, it's Kara. I've heard about your accident. Why didn't you let me know?'

A few seconds went by before he spoke. A few worrying seconds. Was she doing the wrong thing, phoning him? Did Blake want nothing more to do with her now? Was that why he hadn't told her about his accident?

'I thought you had enough to contend with.'

Had he perhaps thought she wouldn't care? Even hearing the sound of his voice sent a tingle through her body. 'How are you?'

'Recovering.'

'Can I come and see you? No one seems to know exactly what your injuries are.'

There was a long pause before he answered. And when he did speak his voice was oddly quiet. 'I'd like that.'

'I'll be there straight away—if that's OK?' It seemed important to her that she should not wait. Though if she had stopped to ask herself why she would not have been able to give an answer. She ought not to care. But she did. She loved Blake despite everything, and she was concerned for him—she wanted to see for herself what his injuries were.

'Only if you let me send my driver for you. I'm not sure your car will make the journey here and back.'

Kara smiled into the phone. Her car was so old that it was a wonder it hadn't given up the ghost a long time ago.

When she arrived at Blake's house she was let in by his housekeeper. 'I'm warning you, Kara, he is not a good patient—he's very grouchy. You'll find him in his study. His injuries haven't stopped him playing with his computer.'

Playing! What Kara saw on the screen as she entered the room was columns of figures. He was working.

Naturally. She might have known it would take a lot to keep Blake away from his work.

The moment she looked at him, the moment her eyes met his, Kara knew that it had been a mistake to come. No matter how she tried, she could not hate him. The love inside her flowed through her limbs like warm honey. All she wanted to do was go to him and feel his arms around her. She wanted back the man she had fallen in love with in Italy.

'What happened, Blake?' she asked quietly, walking towards him. Apart from some marks on his face she could see no other sign of injury.

'I'm sure you don't really want to know.'

'Of course I do,' she said at once. 'I wouldn't be here otherwise.'

Blake shook his head and closed his eyes, as if reliving the scene. 'It was the night I last saw you. I couldn't sleep. So I decided to take the car out—anywhere. I didn't care. I drove too fast. But it was the drunken idiots in the other car who caused the accident. A head-on collision. I was lucky. I have five broken ribs as well as some pretty bad bruises.'

'Five?' she asked in horror. 'Oh, Blake!' Instinct made her go to him and rest her hand across his shoulder. She bowed her face to his and touched her lips to his cheek. 'I'm sorry—so sorry.'

'It was not your fault,' he growled.

Kara felt that it was. 'If you hadn't been angry at me then you wouldn't have driven so fast.'

'Come here.' He urged her down on his lap, his mouth seeking hers, and Kara did not have the strength to refuse him. Her blood burned hot and strong as his kiss deepened, and every thought that it was wrong to be allowing this after the way he had reacted to her pregnancy disappeared.

All she wanted was his kisses—his hot, hungry kisses. They did more than breathe life into her. They consumed her, made her totally his. Everything else was forgotten. This was the Blake she had known in Italy—the Blake who had taught her the pleasures of the flesh and the intimacy of loving someone.

She heard the soft noises emanating from the back of her throat, felt her body melt against him, and felt too the way he was losing hold. It seemed that his pain was forgotten as he devoured her mouth; all he wanted was to kiss her. And this was what she wanted too. She had missed the passion between them, the sensations that warmed and thrilled her, the knowledge that Blake found her desirable.

Without even realising what she was doing Kara twisted around so that she was straddling his legs, careful not to press against his chest. The look in his eyes was one she remembered well: the glazed look of a man filled with raw need over which he had no control.

She too felt as though she was drowning…swimming against a current too strong to fight. *I love you, Blake*. The words filled her head but she did not speak them— knew that she dared not. Instead she touched her hands to the sides of his face and this time she kissed him, allowing her tongue to explore the shape of his lips, the moist heat inside his mouth, finally touching her tongue to his.

Blake groaned, and his hands came behind her head so that he could take control. His kisses were fierce and deadly, filling her with an emotion that was almost too painful to bear. She needed to remember that this was pure sex. Nothing more. It did not mean that their relationship was back on.

'Kara!' He breathed her name. 'Tell me I have been a fool to ever suspect you.'

Hope filled her. 'You are a fool!' she replied immediately.

'I want to make love to you, Kara, but my ribs—they hurt too much.'

'Then *I* will make love to *you*,' she said.

Her heart beat fast as she slid to her knees and slowly unzipped him, releasing the fastening on his waistband and tugging his trousers down over his hips. His boxers followed, and she almost got up and ran when she saw how hard and ready he was for her.

But she couldn't change her mind now. She had gone too far. And when she began to drop tiny kisses along his thighs, heading towards her target, his hands came down to touch her head, his fingers threading through her hair, holding her so tightly that she could not move even if she wanted to.

She chanced a glance at him and saw that his head had fallen back and his eyes were closed. He looked as though he was already in heaven. Sensing her looking at him, he lifted his lids and met her gaze head-on. 'Don't stop,' he groaned, his eyes glazed with pure emotion.

He had taught her how to pleasure him like this and Kara took her time, exulting in the noises he made, in his involuntary movements. She felt herself growing closer to her own orgasm, and was afraid it might happen before Blake reached his. But it didn't, and when he finally let go it was as though the earth had shifted beneath her feet too.

She stayed where she was, silent and fulfilled, while Blake's hands held her head. It was a deep moment of togetherness.

Blake was not used to admitting that he was ever wrong. But he had been wrong even suspecting for one second that Kara would look at another man. If there was someone else she would not have been able to do what she had just done. She would not even have come here. She cared. It had been a gesture of love.

Love! The forbidden word.

Even before today, before she had arrived and self-lessly put his needs before her own, he had berated himself. He had been judge and jury without all the facts, without any real evidence. It would be ungentlemanly of him now not to give her the benefit of the doubt.

'I am sorry I misjudged you. I should have known that—'

Kara closed his lips with her finger. 'Please, say no more. Don't spoil the moment.'

In response he took the tips of her fingers into his mouth. 'I've been a complete swine. Do you forgive me?'

'Of course.'

'Then will you stay a while and keep me company?'

Kara nodded.

'I do not deserve you, Kara,' Blake said, before capturing her head and kissing her.

In the days that followed Blake surprised himself by feeling more content than he ever had in his life. He was even beginning to think that against his better judgement he had fallen in love again—with Kara. His initial reservations about becoming a father were fading into the background.

And when he went with her to the obstetrician there was no doubt in his mind that he wanted to be a permanent part of their child's life. He wanted to watch him grow every step of the way. He would play with him in a way his father never had.

And he wanted Kara beside him.

He was going to ask her to marry him.

CHAPTER TEN

KARA could not wait to get home and tell her mother how her appointment with the obstetrician had gone—how excited Blake had seemed. But the instant she walked into the house and saw her mother's pale, worried face, the way that she was shaking uncontrollably, everything else went out of her head.

She crossed the room in seconds, her heart pounding. 'What's the matter?' Her mother's skin looked almost grey, and Kara feared that she was about to suffer a heart attack. 'I'll call the doctor.'

Her hand went towards the phone but her mother stopped her. 'He's been here.'

'Again?' She knew very well who her mother meant, and her already fast heartbeat increased. 'Why? What does he want now?' His visits were becoming far too frequent for Kara's peace of mind, and she was afraid that all the worry would affect her baby.

Lynne pulled a face. 'He's seen Blake coming and going more often lately. He knows he's rich. He's upping the payments again.'

When her mother mentioned by how much Kara gasped. 'But that's more than I earn. He can't do that.

What did you tell him?' She feared that their nightmare was never going to end.

'That our circumstances haven't changed. Not that he believed me.'

'You shouldn't have opened the door to him.'

'I didn't know it was him,' said Lynne, her eyes pained. 'I thought it was you and that you'd forgotten your keys. He shouldered his way in, Kara. I was terrified!'

'We need to call the police,' said Kara at once. 'He can't do this. It's gone too far.'

'The police can't do anything, Kara,' her mother said, fear evident in her voice. 'The contract he has is legal, remember? He'll deny using threats against us and it will be our word against his. But there might be a solution,' she added, lifting her brows and looking at her hopefully. 'You could ask Blake to lend us the money so we can be rid of him once and for all.'

'Ask Blake?' Kara closed her eyes and shook her head. Getting pregnant by him was embarrassing enough. To ask for money to solve their personal problems would be a step too far.

'I feel so foolish for having let it get this far. And I hate that I have involved you. But I do not think my heart can stand much more.'

Tears filled Lynne's eyes now, and Kara held her mother close. To ask Blake would be painful and humiliating in the extreme. And yet her mother was right. He was in a position to help. And then the loan shark wouldn't be on their backs all the time, demanding payment. It would be a fair deal. They would know exactly where they stood. But it was still an awful lot to ask of him. He'd only just got over the shock of the baby.

'You could tell him that it's to buy stuff for the baby,' said her parent. 'Men have no idea how much these things cost, so I'm sure he won't ask questions.'

The amount she needed to borrow would buy an awful lot of baby things, thought Kara. But because her parent still looked pale and fragile, her breathing difficult, as though she was indeed on the verge of a heart attack, Kara finally reluctantly nodded. 'Very well. I'll ask him.'

Her mother's relief was instant and some of the colour returned to her face. 'You're a good girl, Kara, and I'm sorry to have to burden you with this.'

It was going to be the hardest thing she had ever had to do. Telling Blake that she was pregnant would be nothing compared to this.

When she went to work the next morning she went straight into Blake's office. It was no good sitting thinking about it. She had to ask him immediately.

'What's wrong?' His grey eyes scanned her face. 'You look pale. Are you not feeling well? If that's the case you shouldn't have come to work.'

He looked so concerned, so very concerned, that Kara almost backed out. How could she do this? But seeing her mother's pale and anxious face in her mind's eye was a warning that she *had* to go through with it.

'I'm all right,' she insisted. 'It's just that I need to ask you a favour—a very big one.' Her heart raced, thumping so hard that it felt as if it was trying to burst out of her chest. Perspiration gathered under her arms, and her whole body was pulsing with anxiety.

'Ask away,' he said. 'Is it something to do with your mother? I thought she didn't look very well the last time I saw her.'

'I—I need some money, Blake,' she said, not answering his question. 'I wouldn't ask if it wasn't necessary.' She swallowed the lump that had gathered in her throat and forced herself to look at him. She didn't want Blake guessing how hard this was for her. She had lain awake all night worrying. But her mother's health was at stake here. She was left with no choice. It was either asking Blake to help or ending up losing her home or her mother—possibly both.

'But of course. What was I thinking? You need to buy things for the baby.'

Relief flooded her that she did not have to actually lie. 'You've no idea how much they cost these days.' How could she sound so normal when every nerve tingled with fear? When the blood pumped hotly and uncontrollably around her body? Never in her life had she done anything like this, and she hoped she never had to do so again. Fear froze her limbs and dried her mouth, and she was sure he must see how uneasy she was.

'I will open a bank account for you at once. Shall we say five thousand pounds?'

Kara closed her eyes. How could she tell him that that was not enough? That she wanted five times that amount? It was difficult to comprehend how the sum her father had initially borrowed in her mother's name had grown to that amount. But it had. Interest had piled on top of interest, and now they were facing dire consequences if it was not repaid. There was no one else she could turn to except Blake.

When his finger lifted her chin she shuddered, opening her eyes, feeling her throat close up as she stared into the darkness of his gaze. His brow was furrowed but he spoke softly. 'What is wrong, my beautiful Kara?'

'It's not enough,' she whispered.

She felt the way his body grew tense, even though his expression did not change. 'Not enough? Pray tell me what you are going to buy for this baby of ours?'

The inflection in his voice worried her. 'There are lots of things,' she said hesitantly. 'A pram, a cot, a pushchair, clothes—all sorts. I need to turn a room into a nursery, so there'll have to be new furniture. I'll need about twenty-five thousand pounds.' Her heart was thumping so loud she feared it would jump out of her chest.

He looked long and hard into her eyes, making Kara wish herself a thousand miles away. Never in her life had she felt as embarrassed and as uncomfortable as she did at this moment. She had promised her mother, though, and she had to go through with it.

'And do you really think I believe that's how much things for a baby costs?' he asked, his voice taking on an even harder edge. 'I would suggest—' his fingers dug deeply into her forearms, bruising, hurting, but she did not flinch '—that this is for your own personal gain. Am I right?'

His eyes burned into her, and Kara felt her insides begin to shrivel, but she could not let her parent down. 'You may think what you like, Blake, but I am not in the habit of begging for money without just cause.'

Blake hated the way he was thinking, but it very much looked as though Kara had had a taste of the high life and found that she liked it—that she preferred it to the simple life she led with her mother, and was now trying to cash in on it. He did not know how much it cost to prepare for a baby, but he was damn sure it wasn't nearly as much as Kara was asking. It was not that he minded giving her money for his unborn child, but he did not like being taken for a fool.

Unbidden memories of Melanie flashed into his mind. Melanie trying to pass off another man's child as his. Melanie wanting a share of his wealth. And once the idea was implanted he could not get rid of it. He could not ignore the fact that he had seen Kara on her doorstep in the arms of another man.

He had found it difficult to accept her story that he was a friend of her mother's—the woman lived a solitary lifestyle. He had been deeply suspicious at the time, but had nevertheless given her the benefit of the doubt. Even apologising for questioning her.

It hurt to think that he had been so wrong. He truly had thought Kara was different. Damn it, he had been going to ask her to marry him. She had got beneath his skin in a way he had never expected—or even wanted.

And now this! What was it about him that made women think he was an easy target? The Melanie incident had made him wary, and he had stuck to his guns all these years. So why had he let his guard down now? Why had he let Kara creep into his life and into his heart?

She was looking at him now as though she wished that she had never asked. As well she might! Every vestige of colour had left her face. He wanted to tell her to go, to get out of his life. His disappointment was a hard and bitter pill to swallow.

'And that cause would be…?' he asked grimly, hoping against hope that he had once again jumped to the wrong conclusion.

'I can't tell you Blake.' Kara hung her head, her devastating shame complete.

'You cannot? Or you do not want to?' He let his eyes rest on her face for several long seconds, and when there was no answer, when she refused to look him in the eye, when she looked miserably down at her feet instead, he said grimly, 'Let me tell you what *I* think, Kara. I think you are trying to play me for a fool. I think you are using the baby you are carrying for financial gain. I think you are trying to trick me as Melanie once tried, and—'

'How dare you?' Fire immediately lit Kara's eyes, and she flashed them into his face. 'I would *never* do a thing like that. This *is* your baby and you'd better believe it. Forget about the money, Blake. I can see that it was a mistake asking for your help.'

He looked into her face, seeing a mixture of both anger and despair, and for some reason it created deep unease inside him. What he should be doing was kicking her out of his life. Instead he found himself making a proposition.

'I *will* give you the money—but on one condition. You move in with me permanently.' He might be crazy suggesting it, but he could not easily dismiss her. Despite his disappointment that she had tried to make money out of this situation, she had got beneath his skin in a way none of the others had. Blake was convinced there was something else going on here, and he was determined to get to the bottom of it. Why did she want so much money? There was only one way to find out, and that was to keep her as close to him as possible.

'Move in with you?' For just a moment hope bloomed in Kara's chest. Hadn't she wanted this all along? To live with Blake? To have a future with him? But as she looked at the coldness in his eyes now she saw that he was not offering her a future. He was offering her a prison. He would own her in return for the money. Would men always be in control of her life? First her father, then the loan shark and now Blake. If she accepted Blake's offer of the money she might be free of one shackle around her neck, but she would simply be replacing it with another one. She knew what her answer must be. 'I can't do that, Blake.'

Blake thought for a moment. Her answer had confused him. If she moved in with him then she would be given exactly the kind of lifestyle she wanted—one far removed from the life she had now. So why was she turning his offer down? Did she need the money for another purpose than funding her lifestyle? What was she keeping from him?

He couldn't help wondering whether her mother was in on the act too. The moment the thought entered his mind he put it into words. 'Does your mother know about this request for money? Is she a part of this *let's see what we can get out of Blake* plan?' And the way Kara flinched, the way she averted her eyes, looking anywhere but at him, the way hot colour came rushing back into her face, told him exactly what he wanted to know.

Disappointment flooded him in cruel waves. He felt

as though someone had taken a knife to his heart and sliced it in two. The once innocent Kara, his PA who had served him in a quietly efficient way, had turned into a carbon copy of every other woman he had dated.

If it wasn't for the fact that she was carrying his baby he would send her packing right here and now. He might be many things but he wasn't cruel enough to do that. He would tell her, though, that she would not get a penny more out of him than was necessary for the upbringing of his child—not until he found out exactly why she wanted so much money.

'I'm sorry I asked.' Kara had never felt so humiliated in her life. The look in Blake's eyes made her want to turn and run and never see him again. She had known all along that it would be a bad idea asking him for money, but foolishly she had never expected it to turn out like this. She had naively hoped that Blake would simply hand over the cash, no questions asked. But this was Blake Benedict, businessman extraordinaire! Once again Kara realised how badly she had misjudged his feelings towards her.

'And I am sorry you asked too,' he said, the quietness in his voice more deadly than when he had raised it. 'Shall we start work?'

Kara would have liked nothing more than to turn around and run. She had demeaned herself for nothing. She wanted to walk out of the office and never see Blake again. But that would mean losing her job, and she could ill afford that—especially now. She was not sure, though, how she was going to get through the rest of the day. At least it was Friday, so she would have the weekend to come to terms with her humiliation.

The atmosphere between them was decidedly icy, and it was a relief when Blake was called away early.

When she got home and told her mother that he had refused to lend them the money, deliberately omitting the fact that he had suggested she move in with him, Lynne broke down in tears. 'What are we going to do now?'

Fearing for her parent's health, Kara put her arms around her and held her close. 'We're going to forget about it for the time being. I'll make us a nice cup of tea, and we'll watch TV and push Blake and the loan shark and everyone else right out of our minds.'

It was easier said than done, but at least Lynne calmed down, and on Saturday Kara suggested some retail therapy. 'Even if we only window shop,' she added, 'it will do you good to get out of the house.'

They had a good day—Kara even managed to forget about Blake. She had spent the whole night tossing and turning, reliving her humiliation at his expense. Deep down inside she knew she couldn't blame him for refusing her the money, since she hadn't told him the truth about what it was for. It was ridiculous to have expected him to believe that it was all for the baby.

But her mother's sanity meant more to her than anything else. Lynne was a very private woman who kept herself very much to herself. She had always hidden from her neighbours the way her husband treated both her and her daughter, and over the years they had learned not to ask questions.

And so Kara felt that it was only right that she respect her mother's privacy, even though it had made it hard asking Blake for help. She could still feel the deep humiliation. She had wanted to turn tail and run and never see him again. What they would do when she finally had to leave work because of the baby Kara did not know—how would she ever repay the debt then? But she refused to think about it. Her main concern was her mother, and for her sake she needed to keep bright and cheerful.

Except 'bright and cheerful' flew out of the window when the loan shark decided to pay them yet another visit. They'd had a good day at the shops, even buying only the very cheapest of baby clothes had lifted their spirits and they had been in a good mood when they arrived home.

It was early evening when the doorbell rang, and unsuspectingly Kara went to open the door—only to be confronted by the man who held a tight grip over their lives. Quickly Kara stepped outside and closed the door behind her, so that her mother would not know who stood there.

'Do you have the money?' he growled.

'If you mean can I give you any more than we are already doing, then the answer is no,' said Kara bravely, even though inside she was quaking with fear. She knew that this man was not averse to using force to get what he wanted. 'And if you do not stop harassing us I shall call the police.'

Her brave words had no effect. His top lip rose scornfully, his narrow eyes ugly and condemning. 'This is a legitimate loan. There is nothing they can do.'

'But you cannot keep upping the payments or threatening us in this way.' She felt that her protest was in vain, but she had to try something. 'We can't pay you money we haven't got.'

'You're forgetting the rich boyfriend,' he jeered, his breath smelling of tobacco and something as unpleasant as the man himself. 'Don't think I haven't seen you with him. What I'm asking for would be a pittance in his eyes. Ask him for it.'

'I can't do that,' she declared, surprised to hear her voice still coming out strong and steady when all hell was still breaking out in her body. Her heart was thumping like a mad thing and every pulse stampeded. 'I refuse to involve someone else in your fraud. The only people I'm prepared to go to are the police.'

Strong hands gripped her shoulders and he thrust his face up close. 'I want my money.'

And she wanted him to leave her alone. She pushed as hard as she could against his chest and he let her go—but not before he had made a further threat. 'I'll come back every day until I get what I want. You'd better believe it.'

'And if you do that I will definitely go to the police. *You'd* better believe *that*.'

Not until the door was safely shut behind her did Kara feel safe. She leaned back against it, breathing deeply, forcing herself to calm down before she faced her mother again.

CHAPTER ELEVEN

A SLEEPLESS night had left Blake tired and out of sorts. He could not shut Kara out of his mind. Deep down inside he did not want to believe that she was capable of feathering her own nest at his expense. He couldn't help wondering whether there was some other reason why she had asked him for such a large amount of money. But what? He paid her a good wage, she and her mother lived comfortably, so why the need for more? It was puzzling in the extreme.

When Kara had changed from a mouse into a beautiful woman she had delighted him. She had tugged at a corner of his heart. She had almost made it her own. Almost! Thank goodness he hadn't got to the point of asking her to marry him. Wouldn't that have been a grave error of judgement? He'd thought he had learned his lesson when Melanie deceived him. Now he realised that he was still vulnerable. And vulnerability meant mistakes.

Over and over he asked himself the question whether he knew Kara at all. Whether he had ever really got to know her. Discovering her avaricious side was not a pleasant thing. It had angered and dismayed him. Nevertheless he felt disquiet about the way he had handled the situation. Maybe he should go and see her, talk to her in her own surroundings, try to find out exactly why she wanted so much money.

He had been due to go out to dinner with a banker friend, but at the last minute he cancelled, deciding that a visit to Kara was more important. If he left it until tomorrow he would have another night without sleep. He needed to sort this matter out once and for all.

Even so he felt an unexpected quickening of his senses as he neared her house. Whatever he might think of Kara now, there was no getting away from the fact that she was expecting his baby. It was the hardest thing he had ever had to accept—and it still gave him nightmares. He had never seen himself as a family man—never wanted to be a family man. Which was why he found it hard to believe that it was happening to him now.

Because he did not want her to see him coming, to give her time to decide what she would say to him, he parked in an adjoining street. But as he rounded the corner he could not believe what he saw. Kara in the arms of that man again!

His blood began to boil—until he looked more closely and saw that this was no cosy clinch, as he had first imagined. The man was hostile. It looked as though he was actually threatening Kara!

Blake hastened his step, but before he got close the man let her go, sliding into his car and driving swiftly away. And while he watched the man leave, making a mental note of his number plate, Kara disappeared inside the house.

He wasn't going to let this go, though. And he wasn't

going to be satisfied until Kara told him exactly what was going on. He strode along the street and banged on the door. He wasn't surprised when no one opened it. She was probably scared that the man, whoever he was, had returned.

So he phoned her. 'Kara, it's me. I'm outside. Let me in.'

A moment's silence before she spoke. 'What are you doing here?' she asked, and he thought he heard tears in her voice.

'I need to speak to you.'

'I don't want to speak to you. Go away.'

'I'm going nowhere,' he declared firmly. 'Open the door, Kara, before I break it down.' He wouldn't have done that, of course, but it worked. He heard the key being turned in the lock, heard a bolt being withdrawn, and the thought that she needed to lock and bolt herself in turned his stomach. Who was this man, and why was he harassing her?

Kara's white and drawn face shocked him. He immediately wanted to pull her into his arms and tell her that whatever it was that was happening in her life he would take care of it. But he guessed that she wouldn't let him.

'What are you doing here?' she asked again.

'I came to talk about the money you asked me for. But it has begun to look as though there are far more important things to talk about. Who was that man?'

If Kara's face could have gone any paler then it did. Her eyelids closed for a few seconds, and when she clutched the wall for support he put an arm about her shoulders and led her into the sitting room, where her mother also looked as though she was on the verge of collapse.

Once Kara was seated he sat down himself, looking from her to her mother and back again. 'Are you going to answer my question?'

Kara closed her eyes for a moment before looking at her mother. 'Can we have a little privacy, please?'

'Kara, are you sure this is for the best?'

'Mum, we can't go on like this any longer. I have the baby to think of now, and things are only going to get harder for us. I have to tell Blake.'

Lynne actually looked relieved as she nodded and left the room.

Once they were alone Kara told Blake the whole story—about the loan her father had taken out in her mother's name, about the payments constantly rising. 'It's a never-ending nightmare,' she added, once she had finished.

'And this is why you wanted all that money?'

She nodded, her arms folded across her chest, her eyes sadder than he had ever seen them.

'Why didn't you tell me before, Kara? I could have sorted all this mess out for you!'

'Because my mother did not want anyone to know,' she answered with a wry twist to her lips. 'It's very shameful to have been duped by the man she once loved, the man she married. She would have been deeply embarrassed. She's not the sort of person to share her problems with strangers.'

Blake wanted to take her into his arms and comfort her, but he felt that was not the right thing to do considering the way he had spoken to her yesterday. She would probably push him away, and he did not want that.

His deepest concern at the moment was the degenerate who was doing this to them. Anger had risen in him as she spoke—anger that any man could prey on two helpless females the way this man did. He played on their fear, driven by greed, uncaring that he was making their lives a living hell. And they probably weren't the only people he was harassing.

Neither had he helped by parking his Bentley outside their house! In fact he was the one who had exacerbated their problem. He curled his fingers into his palms. 'Do you know where this guy lives?'

Kara shook her head, at the same time looking quite alarmed. 'You're not thinking of confronting him?'

'Someone has to,' he growled. 'He cannot be allowed to get away with this. What he is doing is unlawful.'

'It doesn't stop him.'

'Of course not. There are plenty of con men like him around. But they usually get their just desserts in the end. He'll come unstuck—you'll see. Meantime, I definitely think you should come and live with me. You *and* your mother. He'll soon give up when he realises that you no longer live here.'

'It's not the answer,' said Kara, although her heartbeats had hastened at the thought. The loan shark would find them wherever they were. The only way they would get this man off their backs was to pay him in full the amount he claimed they owed.

'I'm not giving you a choice.' His grey eyes were relentless on hers. 'You will be safe, both you and your mother, and our baby. I promise you that. I'm not sure that all this stress is good for you or the little one.'

It wasn't good for them, Kara knew that. But she knew that Blake was only offering her his home in order to keep the baby safe and keep her under his spell. The other option was staying here and living with the nightmare of the loan shark everyday.

She had her mother to think of too. All this worry was not doing her health any good. She deserved better. She had put up with so much during her life that it would not be fair to put her through any more. Not when Blake had offered them a lifeline.

'I don't seem to have much choice, do I?' she asked quietly, unaware that her eyes reflected her sorrow.

'Not if you know what's best for you. For you both.'

Kara drew in a long, ragged breath, and released it on a sigh.

'So you agree? You'll move in with me?'

She nodded. 'I'll tell my mother.' She didn't dare look him in the eye. In a way he was saving their lives, but she was not happy about it.

Her mother, though, was both delighted and overwhelmed. 'Thank you, Blake,' she kept saying. 'Thank you, Blake. You have no idea how much this means to me.'

'I think I do,' he answered gruffly. 'What I want you both to do is pack up whatever you'll need for the time being, and I'll organise transport for the rest tomorrow.'

Everything was moving so fast that Kara felt dizzy. Blake took one look at her and ordered her to sit down.

In contrast her mother seemed to have taken on a new lease of life, bustling around, collecting everything she thought they would need.

And finally they left behind the house where so much misery had occurred. Kara knew that this was only going to be an interim period in her life, but she could not help feeling relief. Not that she expected to be entirely happy living with Blake. The closeness they had once shared was gone, and there was no way she could go on living with him permanently. He wouldn't want that either, she felt certain. He was doing his Good Samaritan act but it was only a temporary solution to their problems, and he was really only doing it to ensure his baby was safe.

Her mother, though, was in seventh heaven. 'Whoever would have thought we'd end up living somewhere like this?' she asked. 'Blake's a good man, Kara.'

'It's not permanent, Mum,' said Kara, unaware that there was a sharp edge to her voice. 'I don't want to be beholden to him.'

Lynne frowned. 'How can you be beholden when you're expecting his baby?'

'You're forgetting we're only just about friends. There's nothing between us any more.' Except her heart refused to believe it. It went on the rampage every time he was near. But there was nothing she could do but ignore it—pretend it wasn't happening. The honeymoon period was over. Their relationship was held together by the baby and nothing more.

'Are you sure, Kara?'

'Of course I'm sure. And we're not going to stay here any longer than necessary.'

Lynne's voice was filled with alarm when she spoke. 'We're safe here, Kara. Can't you see that? Safe for the first time in our lives.'

'Yes, but— Well, we'll see,' she accepted reluctantly. She was thinking of herself rather than her mother, which was incredibly selfish. But living with Blake was not her idea of fun.

Later that evening when her mother had gone to bed early, Blake invited Kara to join him for a drink.

'If you make it a hot chocolate,' she said.

A single brow rose. 'I actually like hot chocolate. Mrs Beauman will be delighted. She thinks I drink too much alcohol.'

Such mundane conversation, when Kara guessed he would much prefer to talk about their circumstances. 'My mother really appreciates what you are doing for us,' she said. 'It's as though a whole weight has been lifted from her shoulders.'

Blake nodded. 'I can well imagine it. There was no way I could allow you to go on living there, a perfect target for that unscrupulous money-lender. Why didn't you tell me about him before, Kara?'

'How could I?' she asked. 'He's the biggest embarrassment of our lives. We both felt so ashamed, and we wanted no one to know.'

'As though it was your fault?' he asked with surprising understanding. 'When in fact it was that useless man of a father who got you into this mess?'

Kara closed her eyes. The only good part of her whole life had been the time she'd spent in Italy. Only then had she been able to forget her problems. She'd been the happiest she had ever been. Except that the pleasure she had experienced then had now given way to a whole new set of problems. Unconsciously she put a hand on her stomach.

Blake's eyes narrowed. 'Are you all right, Kara? All this upset cannot be very good for your—for *our* baby.'

'I'm OK,' she said. 'A touch weary, that's all.'

'And is the little man all right?'

Kara could not help but smile. 'He—or maybe *she*,' she corrected, 'is doing fine.'

When his housekeeper came in, setting a tray down on the table beside them, she was still resting her hand on her stomach.

Mrs Beauman's smile was warm and welcoming. 'It's good to see you again, Kara. I hope you and your mother will be very comfortable here. You must tell me if there is anything that you need.'

'I will,' promised Kara.

Their hot chocolate was in a Thermos jug, with two china mugs on the side. Blake leaned forward and filled their mugs.

Kara waited until he had finished before saying, 'Does Mrs Beauman know about the baby?'

Blake shook his head. 'I saw no reason to tell her.'

Because he was ashamed? Because this was an interim period in his life? Kara had no idea what the future held. Of one thing she was certain: she could not go back to their house again. They would need to find somewhere else to live—somewhere they would never be found by the obnoxious man who was harassing them. Maybe even move to a different part of the country.

She had always fancied living in Scotland. That

would be a good place. Far enough away to forget her troubles. But would her mother like it up there? And how would they manage when they had no money?

'Do you still want me to carry on working for you?' she asked. 'Because I would really like to do so.' She did not tell him that it was to try and build up her bank balance and fund their move.

Blake smiled—one of those smiles that turned her heart over and sent a zillion sensations through her body, darting along nerves and arteries, looking for escape but finding none. 'Nothing would please me more, Kara. I will miss you when you stop work to have the baby. You're the best PA any man could ever wish for. It will be hard finding your successor.'

His best PA! Was that all she meant to him? Her pleasure died. He couldn't have made it any plainer that their affair was over, that the only reason they would stay in touch was because of the baby.

She picked up her mug of chocolate and cradled it between her hands, and as silence settled between them she wondered whether she was jumping to the wrong conclusion. Blake had been talking about work, not their personal life.

It was her hormones. They were all over the place. She did not know what to think any more. So much had happened today that all she longed for now was sleep. Peaceful, refreshing sleep. It would be the first night in a long time that their money worries hadn't troubled her.

'Would you mind very much if I went to bed?' she asked as soon as she had finished her drink. She had sipped it so quickly that her mouth stung. 'It's been quite a day and I'm tired.'

'But of course,' he said at once, standing up.

He held out his hands and she had no option but to take them. And when he had pulled her to her feet he pressed a kiss to her brow. 'Sleep well, Kara.'

And that was it. No arms around her, no holding her close, no mouth-to-mouth contact. It was the sort of kiss you'd give a friend, but not a lover. She might as well get used to the idea that their situation had changed. That Blake no longer wanted her in his bed. She was ultimately going to be the mother of his child, and he would see her all right, but as for anything else…

CHAPTER TWELVE

BLAKE had tried to appear calm and in control for Kara's sake, but inside he was seething that any man could stoop so low as to put the fear of hell into two defenceless women. Kara was even more vulnerable at the moment. He had seen how distraught she was, how terrified, and the thing that hurt most was that *he* had had a part to play in it.

He had not stood by her when she came to him for help. He had been brutally angry instead, believing the very worst of her. And although she was grateful to him for rescuing them he sensed that she had lost all faith in him in every other respect. He was almost afraid to touch her, in case she brushed him away. Rejection was not something he could handle. The fact was that whatever had been growing between them was gone. Ruined by his own stupidity.

He bowed his head in his hands, wondering how he could go on working with her, having her live in his house, without ever being able to touch or kiss her. Or bed her. It was a fate too hard to contemplate.

But first things first. He needed to sort out the villain who had been blighting their lives.

* * *

It did not take him long to discover who he was and where he lived, and on Monday evening after work, after he had taken Kara home and knew that she was safe, he drove to the man's house.

A very fine house. Bought, decided Blake, feeling renewed anger rise in his throat, on the proceeds of his underhand, heartless treatment of innocent people. A woman answered the door—an over-made-up blonde, wearing a low-cut blouse and a tight black skirt. 'Yes?'

'I've come to see Mr Draydon.'

'And who shall I say is calling?'

'Benedict. Blake Benedict. And tell him I'm in a hurry.'

When she moved to shut the door Blake put his foot in the way. It had been a telling action, suggesting that he wasn't the first caller to want to see this man.

Blake's grey eyes were hard when the loan shark finally appeared. He had taken so long that Blake was on the verge of entering the house and seeking him out.

'Yes?' Already he seemed on the defensive.

'Mr Draydon?'

'That's right. Do I know you?'

'Not until this moment. But I think you will remember me for some time to come.'

The man frowned.

'Do you get a great deal of satisfaction from frightening defenceless women? Extracting money from them that they can ill afford? I'm actually talking about one woman in particular, but it's my guess that she's not the only one you're trying to defraud.'

The man's eyes narrowed. 'I have no idea what you're talking about.'

'No? Does the name Mrs Redman ring a bell?'

Blake saw the flash of enlightenment in the man's eyes before he blanked it off. 'She is on my books, yes.'

'And for how long has she been "on your books"?'

'What are you getting at?' he asked with a sudden snarl. 'And what's it to do with you?'

'I am suggesting,' said Blake loudly and firmly, ignoring his question, 'that you are illegally demanding money from her and her daughter. I am suggesting that the loan has already been paid many times over. I have seen the original documents and I know how much you have taken from them. I'd now like to see your books.'

This was Blake on the warpath. Blake in his immaculate handmade suit and silk shirt. Blake with an expression so hard it might have been carved out of stone, causing the other man to lose some of his bravado.

'If you do not comply I shall not hesitate to go to the police,' he added, not for one second allowing his eyes to drop from the other man's.

'You'd better step in.' Mr Draydon's eyes darted this way and that, checking to see whether anyone was watching.

Perhaps, thought Blake, this was not the first time he had had some irate client turning up on his doorstep.

Inside, the house was as Blake had guessed it might be—filled with expensive furniture, clearly bought with his ill-gotten gains. But he made no comment, simply standing and waiting while the man went to find the necessary paperwork.

What Blake saw, what he read, the figures that leapt out of the pages at him, tripled his heart-rate. He wanted to lash out at the man. He wanted to make sure he never did this to anyone again. The sum of money that Kara and her mother had paid him over the years compared to the sum of the original loan—including interest—went far beyond anything he had expected.

This man was a crook—an out-and-out crook—and he deserved to be behind bars. But that was not why he was here. He was here for Kara's sake. Kara and her mother.

'I think you will agree,' he said, his tone so cold and hard that it would have flattened a lesser man, 'that their debt has been paid. Actually it has been paid many times over, but we will not go into that. Not now.' He eyed the man threateningly, suggesting that if he did not do as he asked then he would be in even deeper trouble. 'What I want you to do, Mr Draydon, is tear up those documents right here in front of me, and let's have an end to this. Otherwise, as I said, I'll get the police involved. This is nothing short of fraud.'

By the time Blake had finished speaking the man had begun to look very nervous. 'It is an unfortunate oversight on my part. I will give you the papers. You can do with them what you like.'

'How generous—considering how much you've conned out of the Redmans,' said Blake, his voice infused with such sarcasm that it was a wonder it didn't flatten the man. In front of him he tore each piece of paper into quarters, before stuffing them into his own pocket. 'Goodbye, Mr Draydon. I wish never to see you again.'

Once in his car, Blake sank back into the seat, closing his eyes for a few seconds, letting his breath out. How he had kept his hands to himself he did not know. The man should be in jail, not living the high life on his proceeds from a crooked business. But at least he had got him off Kara and her mother's back. That was the main thing. They could live safely now, without any fear of some rogue money-lender knocking on their door.

Except he did not want them to leave—at least he didn't want Kara to leave. He had done the unthinkable and fallen in love with her. Despite the vows he had made to himself, he had fallen in love!

The discovery rocked him.

Blake knew that Kara was loyal, trustworthy, kind—and she was carrying his baby! Not that that was the key factor. He would have loved her even if she wasn't pregnant. He had never met anyone like her, and he doubted he ever would again. The thing was, did he stand a chance with her? Or had he ruined everything when he had turned down her plea for help when she needed it most?

The house felt empty without Blake. Kara knew that she ought to feel relieved he had gone out, but instead she wandered from room to room, not knowing what to do with herself. Her mother was content to sit in her bedroom and watch television. She was used to smaller spaces, she said, and the size of the house overwhelmed her.

But Kara could not sit still. She paced up and down

like a caged animal, and when Blake finally returned she wanted to run to him, wrap her arms around him and feel his strength flow into her. But she did none of this. She simply looked at him and smiled weakly.

He had such gorgeous eyes, but she thought they looked tired at this moment and she wondered where he had been. Not that she dared ask. It was, after all, none of her business. It wasn't work-related, she knew that—because *she* always kept his diary up to date.

'Have you eaten?' she asked.

Blake shook his head. 'I'm not hungry, Kara. Come and sit with me. Are you happy here?'

Kara frowned, wondering why the odd question. 'I'd obviously be happier at home,' she told him quietly, 'but not under our present circumstances.'

Her answer seemed to disappoint him, but it was the truth. Living with him but not *being* with him, not making love with him, was sheer hell. She wanted to cry because what they had once had was gone. She could not understand why he had changed from an attentive lover to someone who was almost a stranger. He was polite and correct, and this wasn't the Blake she knew—the Blake she had fallen in love with.

Unhappily, the next few days followed the same pattern. At the office it was pure business, and at home he was kind and courteous—but nothing more. Her mother still stayed in her room, believing she was doing the right thing leaving them together, and Kara did not tell her what was really going on.

So she was not entirely surprised by his question one

evening over dinner. 'Would you prefer to go home, Kara?'

'Is this a trick question?' she asked with a frown. 'You know I would. But how can I?'

He drew in a long breath and said quietly, 'You have nothing to fear any more.'

Her frown deepened. 'I don't understand.'

'The whole issue of the loan has been sorted. Mr Draydon, your loan shark, won't bother you any more.'

Kara felt her mouth fall open. 'He won't?' It was a stupid question, but what was she supposed to say? 'How do you know?'

He smiled grimly. 'I went to see him. He's written off your loan.'

Kara knew the money-lender wouldn't have agreed as easily as Blake was suggesting, but hope began to rise in her heart. 'How did you find him?' In all these years she had never known where he lived.

'Ways and means,' he said dismissively. 'The point is that you and your mother are free of any debt. You have nothing more to fear.'

'Oh, Blake.' Instinctively Kara rose and rushed around the table, throwing her arms around him. 'Thank you. Thank you from the bottom of my heart. You are a wonderful man, Blake. Thank you again.' And before she could stop herself she was kissing him.

But it was a short-lived kiss. He gently put her from him. 'I think you ought to tell your mother.'

'I will—I will in a minute. She'll be as relieved as I am. I can't thank you enough, Blake. This is a dream come true. We can go home now and get out of your hair. Of course, once the baby's born I'll always let you see him.' She missed the pain that crossed his face. 'And you can come with me for the scans. I don't want to deny you any part of our child's life.'

Realising that she had been talking too quickly and not taking any notice of Blake's reaction, Kara pulled up short when she saw the hurt in his eyes. 'I'm sorry. I'm getting carried away, aren't I?'

'I don't want to just come for the scans, Kara. I want to be with you every step of the way. I have to confess that being a father scares the hell out of me, but what scares me more is the thought of losing you. I love you. I love both you and our unborn child.'

Kara could hear the words, but she wondered whether she was imagining them. Whether she was hearing what she wanted to hear and not what he was actually saying. 'You love me?' she asked, knowing that she must sound stupid—but this had come like a bolt from the blue.

'With every breath in my body.'

'But—But—'

'But nothing, Kara. It's true. You've bewitched me. You've changed me. I doubted myself for a while, but now more than anything I want you by my side for always. I want this child and I want more children with you. I know I'm jumping the gun here, but...'

Kara closed her eyes, hardly listening to him now, letting her breath out in a slow, steady stream. She found it hard to believe that this was happening. Blake loved her. He loved her unconditionally. How magical was that?

And then he kissed her. And the magic continued un-abated. And when they went upstairs to tell her mother that a wedding was in the offing Lynne said that she had known all along that it would happen.

'It was just a matter of time,' she said.

Two years later Kara and Blake were out walking in Hyde Park, pushing their twins' pushchair alongside the Serpentine, discussing what name they should give to the baby she was expecting in three months' time. It was going to be a girl—a little sister to Ben and Mark. The twins, who had come as a shock to both of them, had been named after Blake's father.

'I think,' he said now, 'that it's only fair she should be named after your mother.'

Her mother would be over the moon, thought Kara. She had moved back into her little house, finding Blake's mansion far too intimidating, and she was truly happy for the first time in her life. Even her health seemed to have improved.

'Her middle name's Rosemary,' said Kara. 'We could call her Rose. I think I'd like that.'

'Then Rose it will be,' he said. 'She'll be like a beautiful flower—the same as her mother. I love you, Kara, so very, very much. I never thought I'd be this happy.'

'I love you too, Blake Benedict. You're my hero—do you know that? You rescued me from my miserable life when I thought there was never going to be any escape. I shall love you to the end of my days.'

'And I shall love *you*, my adorable Kara—to the end of *my* days.'

MODERN

PASSION AND THE PRINCE
by Penny Jordan

Prince Marco di Lucchesi can't hide his haughty disdain for Lily Wrightington—or his violent attraction to her! Can he trust himself to offer the protection she seeks *without* unleashing his passion?

ALESSANDRO'S PRIZE
by Helen Bianchin

Determined to get on with her newly single life, a break in Milan sounds ideal to Lily Parisi. Until she bumps into Alessandro del Marco, an enigmatic face from her past, and her plans come completely undone...

WIFE IN THE SHADOWS
by Sara Craven

In society's spotlight, Count Angelo Manzini bestows dutiful kisses on his apparently biddable new bride, Elena. But behind closed doors, Angelo is captivated by his countess's defiance...

AN INCONVENIENT OBSESSION
by Natasha Tate

Ethan Hardesty has it all...apart from Cate Carrington—the girl he loved and lost. But now the Carrington family's island is up for auction, providing him with the perfect opportunity to take her into the bargain!

On sale from 20th May 2011
Don't miss out!

FOR DUTY'S SAKE
by Lucy Monroe

Angele refuses to become Crown Prince Zahir's unloved wife out of duty; she will let him go free…but on one condition. The proud Sheikh must give her the wedding night she has dreamed of!

MR AND MISCHIEF
by Kate Hewitt

Sardonic Jason Kingsley is used to women falling at his feet, but relationships are not for him. So why does he find Emily Wood, with her misguided belief in the power of love, irresistibly attractive?

THE BROODING STRANGER
by Maggie Cox

Seeking refuge from her past, Karen Ford comes to Ireland with no intention of getting involved with any man. *Especially* not the brooding stranger she meets one fateful day, who makes a shockingly intimate proposition…

THE GIRL HE NEVER NOTICED
by Lindsay Armstrong

Tycoon Cam Hillier requires a date for this season's fundraising party, and turns to his PA, Liz Montrose, in desperation! Cam's never noticed Liz before…but with no sensible suits or glasses for her to hide behind, that's about to change!

On sale from 3rd June 2011
Don't miss out!

Available at WHSmith, Tesco, ASDA, Eason and all good bookshops

www.millsandboon.co.uk

The Privileged and the Damned
by Kimberly Lang

Lily needs a fresh start—and, fingers crossed, she's found one. After all, why would any of the hot-shot Marshall dynasty even *think* to look beyond her humble façade? Until she catches the roving eye of infamous heartbreaker Ethan Marshall...

The Big Bad Boss
by Susan Stephens

Heath Stamp, the ultimate bad-boy-done-good, is now rich, arrogant and ready to raze his family estate to the ground. If Bronte tries to stop him he'll happily take her down with him. For Heath Stamp has gone from bad...to irresistible!

Ordinary Girl in a Tiara
by Jessica Hart

Caro Cartwright's had enough of romance—she's after a quiet life. Until an old school friend begs her to stage a gossip-worthy royal diversion! Reluctantly, Caro prepares to masquerade as a European prince's latest squeeze...

Tempted by Trouble
by Liz Fielding

Upon meeting smooth-talking Sean McElroy, Elle's 'playboy' radar flashes red, and she tries to ignore the traitorous flicker of attraction! Yet are these two misfits the perfect match?

On sale from 3rd June 2011
Don't miss out!

GIVE IN TO
TEMPTATION...

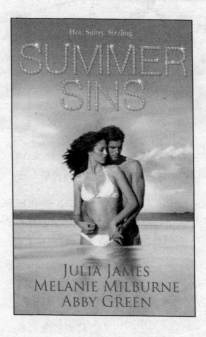

As the champagne flows beneath the glittering sun,
three scandalous affairs ignite...

It's going be one wickedly hot summer of sin!

2 FREE BOOKS
AND A SURPRISE GIFT

We would like to take this opportunity to thank you for reading this Mills & Boon® book by offering you the chance to take TWO more specially selected books from the Modern™ series absolutely FREE! We're also making this offer to introduce you to the benefits of the Mills & Boon® Book Club™—

- **FREE home delivery**
- **FREE gifts and competitions**
- **FREE monthly Newsletter**
- **Exclusive Mills & Boon Book Club offers**
- **Books available before they're in the shops**

Accepting these FREE books and gift places you under no obligation to buy, you may cancel at any time, even after receiving your free books. Simply complete your details below and return the entire page to the address below. You don't even need a stamp!

YES Please send me 2 free Modern books and a surprise gift. I understand that unless you hear from me, I will receive 4 superb new books every month for just £3.30 each, postage and packing free. I am under no obligation to purchase any books and may cancel my subscription at any time. The free books and gift will be mine to keep in any case.

Ms/Mrs/Miss/Mr _____ Initials _____

Surname _____

Address _____

_____ Postcode _____

E-mail _____

Send this whole page to: Mills & Boon Book Club, Free Book Offer, FREEPOST NAT 10298, Richmond, TW9 1BR

Offer valid in UK only and is not available to current Mills & Boon Book Club subscribers to this series. Overseas and Eire please write for details. We reserve the right to refuse an application and applicants must be aged 18 years or over. Only one application per household. Terms and prices subject to change without notice. Offer expires 31st July 2011. As a result of this application, you may receive offers from Harlequin (UK) and other carefully selected companies. If you would prefer not to share in this opportunity please write to The Data Manager, PO Box 676, Richmond, TW9 1WU.

Mills & Boon® is a registered trademark owned by Harlequin (UK) Limited. Modern™ is being used as a trademark. The Mills & Boon® Book Club™ is being used as a trademark.